BUGS
OR PEOPLE ?

BUGS
OR PEOPLE?

by Wheeler McMillen

Appleton-Century
New York

APPLETON-CENTURY
AFFILIATE OF
MEREDITH PRESS

Library of Congress Catalog Card Number: 65-24857
MANUFACTURED IN THE UNITED STATES OF AMERICA FOR
MEREDITH PRESS

Acknowledgments

ONE DOES NOT WRITE A BOOK OF THIS CHARACTER, IN which facts, interpretations, opinions and predictions are involved, by drawing merely upon his own small mental resources. To acknowledge properly all those to whom I am indebted would take pages. I have drawn heavily from publications by the U.S. Department of Agriculture, notably from the 1952 Yearbook of Agriculture, *Insects,* in which thousands of basic facts about insects are assembled. Officials in the Food and Drug Administration, the Agricultural Research Service, Public Health Service and Fish and Wildlife Service have been consulted, and have provided useful publications. Besides their printed materials I have had help from scientific personnel in government, universities, and industries from coast to coast by mail, by telephone, and in interviews. Industrial and trade associations and conservation organizations have been frank to answer tough questions and helpful in other ways. Distinguished authorities on various topics have taken time to read the manuscript and note errors, and have offered highly valuable suggestions. The Agricultural Institute of St. Louis has given important assistance on research problems. This foundation has encouraged the writing of this book as "an important service to consumers and all concerned with providing an abundance of healthful foods of top quality." If these pages present the truth as it is known now, it is because so many generous helpers have made their knowledge available; if the truth, so far as it is known, is not here, the faults are mine.

Wheeler McMillen

Contents

PART THREE:
As of Today and Tomorrow

Introduction

One of the best informed and most responsible editorial writers of his generation in relation to agriculture, the author of this book presents a record and a viewpoint of major significance for the public. The safety, quality, quantity, and cost of our food supply is of interest to everyone. The book will be of immense value also to congressmen and state legislators; for them, as guardians of the public interest, it should be required reading.

From a background of practical farming followed by many years of vigorous leadership in agriculture, the author is in a position to evaluate true progress amidst the urgency for action. He is sensitive to the public interest in terms of health, outdoor recreation, wildlife conservation, the important role of government agencies, and economic relationships at all stages from farms to supermarkets and consumers of food.

Well-established facts and quotations of opinion from bona fide authorities are presented in logical sequence to illustrate the significance of pests that constantly threaten the productivity from plant and animal resources on which human life, health, and cultural progress are dependent. The costs, time factors, safeguards, and regulatory practices related to the production and use of pesticides are presented with a balanced, factual consideration of their great advantages, amounting to necessity, along side the significant but relatively small risks to health, bird life, and aesthetic aspects of our environment.

The valid claims and subtle or gross distortions characteristic of *Silent Spring* are treated sympathetically but accurately. This section of the book alone would justify its publication and wide readership. The foolish, confusing, and unscientific legislation based on so-called "zero tolerances" is reviewed in a very helpful and illuminating way, also. Similar factual treatment is given to the concepts generally associated with organic farming, biological control of pests, and the fear mongering of salesmen and writers who thrive on distortion and distrust—starting typically with a film of truth that covers a mass of assertions that are without substantial evidence. Mistakes in the course of experience are cited and acknowledged in balanced perspective, but without apology or acrimony.

There is a timely discussion also of the urgency to provide for adequate food supplies within each nation, including their relevance to international adjustments without recourse to war but with full recognition of recent and current increases in population.

Valuable features running through the entire manuscript and summarized in the concluding chapters include the citation of desirable and undesirable regulatory policies, together with challenging opportunities that are open for development by research and leadership in the agricultural and food sciences.

Unless the public understands the kind of basic information furnished in an interesting manner by the author, there will be less alertness to, and support for, the continuing need of research and its applications in the agricultural sciences. The need is equally great for public understanding in order to achieve constructive legislation in developing government policies, nationally and internationally.

The problems of agriculture are so closely intervowen with the basic sciences, public health, the chemical industry, economics, and political action, that well-trained leadership and coordination in all these areas will be increasingly important to meet human needs.

Charles Glen King
Associate Director, Institute of Nutrition Sciences, School of Public Health and Administrative Medicine, Columbia University, New York

PART ONE:

Challenges and Choices

1/Enemies of Man

WHOEVER PUT INTO OUR LANGUAGE THAT GLORIOUS phrase, "reverence for life"—was Albert Schweitzer first to use it?—embodied a magnificent concept in three words. As most such expressions do, the phrase probably evokes one idea for you and another for me. Yet, undeniably, "reverence for life" conveys to all of us a thought of the compassion, gentleness, grace, and tenderness that adorn our highest ideals.

The phrase came to mind this morning when I stepped out on the breakfast terrace. From the nearby dogwood branch came an expected, cordial greeting. Timmy, the tufted titmouse, came dancing down twig by twig and spread his wings quickly to alight on my forefinger long enough to make his choice from among the shelled peanuts he knew waited in my outstretched hand. Sleekly efficient, he carried the peanut to a solid branch, fixed it firmly under his toes and rapidly picked it apart. His bright black eyes, jaunty crest and trim gray form, his alert manners, his friendly conversation and his obvious joy in the moment somehow combined to suggest that life is indeed good, an experience of joyous splendor.

Timmy finished his peanut and returned for a second. He probably doesn't weigh as much as an ounce. Plainly every

flit of his tail, every flex of his tiny claws, every lilt in the
notes he whistles from the tall trees, proclaim his ounce to be
truly a fragment of creation designed for respect and worthy
of reverence. Who could shoot or poison Timmy, or ever
permit his glad little life to be shortened by an hour?

As the last fragment of the second peanut disappeared
Timmy turned his bright eye toward a leaf above him and
spotted a small brown caterpillar. Another instant, and he
was off to the tall hemlocks with the caterpillar in his beak.

The caterpillar, too, was alive, but for its wormy life
Timmy displayed no reverence. Much as he likes peanuts, he
balances his diet. Insects, mostly caterpillars and wasps, un-
willingly provide two-thirds of his food. It would be nice to
suppose that Timmy was trying to pay me for his peanuts by
protecting my dogwood from the ravaging worms; but he was
only doing what came naturally.

So, as I turned to my bacon and eggs, I was left to ponder.
Timmy, that ounce of tender beauty and living grace, had
turned ferocious predator when he spied the caterpillar. The
caterpillar may also have been beautiful, as many of them
are; I didn't see it closely enough to appraise its appearance. Perhaps his destiny, had it not been interrupted by
Timmy, was to have become a gorgeous butterfly. It was certain, though, that so far as the dogwood tree was concerned
the caterpillar was out for no good.

Reverence for life? Whose life?

The morning reverie could lead only to the trite and indis-
putable truism that every earthly creature, in its ordained
struggle to survive, must compete with, must consume or
destroy the life of something else. It eats other living things,
crowds them out, or perhaps in the natural pursuit of sustenance carries along the seeds of tragedy.

The yellow fever mosquito, only slightly different from
other mosquitoes, bites only to feed itself, innocent of intent
to destroy man; yet, when itself infected with the fever virus,

can decimate a city. Man, for himself to survive, has learned that he must prevent that mosquito from inhabiting his vicinity. He is no more free from the eternal struggle than Timmy, who must fear the neighbor's cat, or than the caterpillar munching his morning leaf. Timmy, too, is assailed by a mite, by a tick, and by two kinds of lice.

Timmy offers no enmity to the human race. Satisfied with his share of the earth, like nearly all of his avian relatives and most four-footed species, he is content to coexist with man. If we wish to enjoy his grace and beauty, or even contribute a peanut to his living, he doesn't mind. His ancestors for centuries before man became numerous made good titmouse livings for themselves. He makes no threats and proposes no competition.

Along with the fearsome tiger or the gentle antelope, he asks no more than an environment suitable for him to conduct his own life work. Rarely will the business of bird or beast of field or jungle cause him to interfere willfully with the affairs of man.

Not so with the insects!

Insects aggressively invade the domains man marks out for himself. They infiltrate. They seize upon every possible opening. They are pervasive, persistent, penetrating and persevering. They are quick to exploit the bonanzas human beings often arrange for them.

Whether insects or men are best adapted to dominate the earth is a question scientists have raised in all seriousness. The bug has built-in advantages that are not to be scorned.

We human beings incline to suppose that because we have brains and a sort of intelligence, presumably superior to anything else in the known world, we can expect to dominate and survive. We may be assuming too much.

Man came to earth comparatively late. Insects preceded him by countless millions of years. Their survivance is proved. The proud individual who traces his ancestry to William the Conqueror or to Charlemagne, or for all it matters clear back to the primeval Adam, ranks as the merest parvenu, an upstart, compared to the cockroach, whose aristocratic ancestry reaches back into the earliest geological periods. When Adam and Eve arrived the roach was there, waiting to share their garden stuff. Of the fossil insects that have been discovered, about four out of five families or genera are actively in business today.

Man's brain may enable him to keep a little ahead of the insects he must count as his enemies. Fortunately, most of them are harmless to his interests, and many are definitely beneficial. However, the insect has often been and often still is more than a match for man's presumed intelligence.

Whether the insect possesses a faculty that could be termed intelligence or brain remains a moot point. It may be left for the entomologists to consider. Actually, he doesn't need brains. Nature has equipped the insect with so many survival advantages that if he had to make conscious decisions he might be far more vulnerable. A few of these advantages are too interesting not to note here.

First of all, the insect capacity for reproduction and multiplication is incredibly great.

Dr. Leland O. Howard was the great American entomologist of his time (1857–1950). Chief for more than thirty years of the U.S. Bureau of Entomology, he did much original research, especially on flies and mosquitoes. He wrote several books, and spoke widely to warn Americans of what he called "the insect menace," which was also the title of one of his books. Another book was *The House Fly—Disease Carrier*. Characterizing the common house pest as the "typhoid fly," he was largely responsible for sanitation and "swat the fly" campaigns that awakened Americans to the fact that they could not afford to tolerate this abundant and filthy insect.

Dr. Howard demonstrated that one hibernating female fly

could easily provide Washington, D.C., with more than 5½ trillion more flies from April 15 to the end of September. A later writer, Mr. Curtis W. Sabrosky, whose article leads the famous 1952 Yearbook of the Department of Agriculture, *Insects,* considered Howard's statement a little too conservative. "In one summer season from April to August," he says, "the descendants of one pair of house flies, if all lived and reproduced normally, would make a total of 191,000,000,000,000,-000,000." That's 191 quintillion, a figure that perhaps a computer could comprehend. Of course, he points out, not all the eggs and progeny survive.

A Cornell University entomologist, Glenn W. Herrick, produced a still more prodigious figure on insect fecundity. He found that the cabbage aphid averaged forty-one offspring per female between March 31 and October 2, and under New York State conditions had sixteen generations. His female aphid, he calculated, could thus be responsible in one season for a posterity numbering 1,560 sextillion. Quoting Herrick's figures, Sabrosky notes that in the South, where temperatures are more favorable, the cotton aphid or the melon fly could have more generations per year and twice as many offspring.

Herrick also weighed his cabbage aphid. It hefted slightly more than a milligram. So, he calculated, the theoretical maximum of one aphid's descendants, if they all lived to the end of one season, could outweigh the earth's entire human population.

Fantastic and exaggerated as such examples may seem to be, they make their point. While not all species are by any means so prolific, most insects lay large numbers of eggs. Many measure only in days the period from hatching to the time when offspring lay more eggs. Some species do not even wait to mature. The larvae produce other larvae, "just as though a human child," remarks Dr. Howard, "were to give birth to another child."

Most young insects are born educated. No adult needs to watch over them as he grows. They experience no nonproductive years of youth, but immediately proceed to feed themselves and continue to do whatever is necessary, however many stages they must undergo before they become complete adults. (Certain social species, including honeybees, do feed the young.) Many species commit most of their depredations against human society during the juvenile stages.

Neither does the insect world burden itself with nonproductive old age. When the purposes of life have been accomplished, the bug dies. The younger generations bear no responsibility for the elders. No social security, no medical care, no old-age assistance.

The insect profits from his size. An expert at concealment, when his routine demands he can usually make himself virtually invisible to human eyes. He can hide in a crack, crawl under a bit of earth, hang under a leaf, and especially in larval stages make himself at home inside a plant or animal. He may wrap himself up in an inconspicuous cocoon. Even the larger species commonly operate under schemes of protective coloration, which aid them to avoid an enemy's notice.

As a competitor against man for food and space on earth, the very structure of an insect may be reckoned in his favor. He wears his skeleton on the outside instead of within. He gains an advantage by having his digestive and respiratory systems protected by his bones, so to speak; they are inside his skeleton.

At most stages an insect is able to fly or crawl, and even long-distance travel presents him with no problem. All he needs to do is to attach himself to something that is going to move. About half of the injurious insects against which Americans have to contend are foreigners, aliens who have arrived here from other countries. The danger that new pests, injurious to health and food, may invade our borders never ceases; the airplane has enlarged the danger. The federal government maintains a constant vigil to head off the undesirable aliens.

Besides their ability to travel, their spectacular superiority at speedy reproduction, their minute size, skill at hiding, and efficient life processes, the vast numbers and variety of species of insects make these multilegged creatures into formidable contenders for possession of the earth. How many kinds of insects live on our planet no one knows. Scientists' guesses range from 2½ million to ten million. Every year six or seven thousand new species are described, named, and added to the previous total.

Against these millions of insect species, each wonderfully adapted by nature for its particular way of life, man is but one species. Thus far in his progress on earth man has brought to his aid by domestication a very few species of animals, all of which are targets for insect warfare. He has tamed no insects. The nearest he has come to that is his ability to manage, but not truly domesticate, the honeybee.

The insect remains unsusceptible to training. No influence, except his own interest, leads him to change his way of life. Through 250 million years the countless generations have fixed his routines and determined his habits. If they are hostile to human interests, man has no alternatives except to tolerate him, frustrate him, or to attempt his extermination. The insect holds no reverence for life except for his own.

Until barely a century ago, man ignored most of his insect enemies. Being ignorant about them, often even ignorant of their existence, he hardly realized their enmity. He occasionally spanked the mosquito when he felt its bite, scratched his lice and chiggers, and brushed off the fly that tickled his nose. If swarms of locusts destroyed his crops, he knew them only as enemies he could not combat and of whose origin he was unaware. When plagues and fatal fevers scourged his city and killed his family and friends, he considered the disaster to be an act of fate.

To the more recent generations of man scientists have disclosed the deadly facts about the killer insects and have revealed the colossal costs of sharing the earth with these innumerable competitors for sustenance.

Moreover, scientists have placed in man's hands chemical, biological, and other tools that give him a fair chance to fight. The most optimistic entomologists are willing to predict no more at present than occasional and partial victories. These, nevertheless, may often provide assurance—not only against such spectacular disasters as history records but also a margin against much of the damage that the insect hordes, day in and day out, inflict upon the health, comfort and economic interests of their human victims.

Mosquitoes, flies, lice, mites, and fleas convey disease and death to man. Malaria, typhus, and bubonic plague are but three of the murderous bug-borne ailments that each year cause millions to be sick and thousands to die. The human energy that should be advancing man's well-being is sapped by illnesses that can be averted.

We know now that more than half of the earth's people are not well fed. Insects by themselves take an annual four-billion-dollar toll from crop and livestock production in the United States alone, and far more in the world's less agriculturally advanced areas. The food that insects prevent man from producing and using would be enough to raise the nutrition standards for many millions of people.

Let the insects go unchecked? They will go their relentless ways. For humankind they will produce disease and death, poverty, hunger and discomfort. Man has no intelligent choice except to fight back with the best weapons he can command. Even with his best wisdom and knowledge, he may make mistakes; he must try to balance a true reverence for life with the destructive force of the insects, and he will have to take some risks.

2/Birds or People

HOW MANY GENERATIONS OF EAGLES HAD ADDED STICKS TO build higher the huge nest in that tall old pine back from the Florida road no one had ever known. Long before our visits, local folks said, it had been there. For nearly thirty years a part of our winter vacation routine had been to stop by occasionally to see the young eaglets raise their heads or, a little later, to watch them find out what wings were for.

Now a busy shopping center glitters near the road. The tree, the nest, and the eagles are no longer to be seen.

By another back road a little, shallow bayou bulged in from the bay. It must have been rich with the goodies the herons and egrets and shore birds enjoyed, for always many were feeding there and occasionally a rarity appeared. The prized memory of that spot, though, reaches back to the afternoon when we watched a magnificent bald eagle stand thigh deep in the water and, honoring us with no more than an unembarrassed glance, leisurely give himself a thorough bath and preening.

A new street and a row of nice little houses border the bayou now. Only the bolder birds visit it and the eagle, if he still lives, goes elsewhere for his ablutions.

A mile and a half away from the old home farm in northwest Ohio a little pond was hidden, undisturbed, in a secluded corner of a neighbor's land. Cattails and reeds bordered the half-acre of quiet water. Many times my walks to this rare feature in our well-tilled countryside were rewarded by the sight of the little green heron. One year a pair of mallards raised their young there. On one notable day, I had my first close-up glimpses of a great blue heron and of a semipalmated sandpiper, a memorable occasion indeed for a solitary young "ornithologist" with his first bird book in his overalls pocket.

Long ago the little pond was drained and now it is just another corner of another field. Not for miles around can the herons or mallards find a place to pause, much less to nest.

On our own farm, a pasture field for years retained a partially wooded corner in which a pool of water, perhaps a thousand square feet in all, never entirely dried up. One warm April night, standing in the water's edge, kerosene lantern in hand, I watched the bubble-throated toads clamber over the toes of my rubber boots while they showed me how they sing their spring songs. There, another afternoon, I saw my first bittern. Nearby, a hollow basswood tree housed a family of flying squirrels. If I thumped the base with a club, the little beauties would rush to their opening at the top and display their graceful glide to the base of an elm or beech a hundred or more feet away.

A time came when it seemed desirable to turn the pasture into a cornfield. We cleared off the trees and drained the little pool. The corn did well; but no boy since has seen a bittern there, or the flying squirrels.

In those years few birds decorated that Ohio countryside more abundantly than the gorgeously marked black-and-white redheaded woodpeckers. They came in May near corn-planting time, when the oak leaves were about the size of squirrels' ears. Along the rural roads, after the young were airborne (their heads black instead of the adults' rich red) every other telephone pole or fence post seemed to bear a rollicking woodpecker. They liked to light in the roads to pick up insects, and that became part of their tragedy. They were slower than other birds to take flight from the ground; automobiles killed them by the thousands. No longer do so many woodlots provide the dead-tree nesting sites. To find a redhead there now, one must go far from the highways along the more remote and less used roads.

Five years ago, when we moved to our present New Jersey home in the edge of a town noted for its splendid trees and shrubs, a pair of song sparrows greeted us from the old, vine-grown, post-and-rail fence across the road along where the horses pastured. Then the pasture was sold, the bulldozers came, and the song sparrows have given up. Our own shrubs and trees entice the cardinals and catbirds, wrens and jays and titmice, to stay with us, and many others come to visit our feeders, but we still miss the song sparrows.

Destruction of favored habitat becomes each year a more serious problem for wildlife—and a sorrow for people who love the creatures that fly or scamper—a problem of deadly consequence for many species and for multitudes of individuals like those song sparrows. A pair of birds must have a place to nest and a territory in which to range for food. The ceaseless push of people for living space, play space, working space, and moving space each year leaves less room for birds and animals who cannot breed and carry on if they are crowded out of the kind of living accommodations nature prescribes for them.

Seldom—perhaps one could say never—does a developer fill a new block with houses, or a contractor bulldoze the route for a new highway, or a town construct or expand an airport, or a farmer drain a marsh, but a portion of living space has been subtracted from the total that some forms of wildlife, some birds or animals, have for generations regarded as their own territory by rights both of eminent domain and of squatter preemption. How many thousands of little coves and bays and inlets along the shores of the lakes and seas has man appropriated, to the distress of the ospreys and kingfishers and flycatchers to whom these spots have been native homes?

Birds or people—which? How are we to answer such a question? Houses and highways, factories, airports and fields, people must and will have. Displaced persons usually find refuges somewhere; displaced birds cannot always do as well. Bird refuges normally serve only to protect the birds already there. By a heavy dint of community effort we manage here and there to withhold a tract of parkland from the developers, and then usually scrub it up or overrun it until only the treetop birds find it useful. Now and then a farmer will let his fence rows grow so a meadowlark can hide her nest. But in general, man has seldom hesitated to subject any species of creation to his needs nor, for that matter, to his pleasures, which at times have been revoltingly cruel and bloody.

The infinite cruelty of nature herself is a self-evident fact that requires no discourse. The lioness slaughters the harmless zebra because to live, she and her cubs must have meat. The puma stalks and downs the deer. The fox snatches the quail. The hawk devours the mouse and the little screech owl pounces upon the sparrow. The fish leaps for the mayfly, or swallows a lesser fish. This none can condemn. It is all a part of ecology, the mutual relationships between living organisms and their environments. Nature struggles to keep a balance, though seldom succeeding perfectly. One species demands another kind as food upon which to survive; another struggles to preserve itself. Some life is sacrificed that other life may continue.

How valuable is life? Human life, to be specific? Civilized opinion places its worth beyond price, and demands that neither cost nor exertion be spared to preserve and prolong the heartbeat of one living person. Even though hope for health, comfort, or any trace of happiness may have vanished, any purposeful hastening of a human death is proscribed; except, of course, in war or as penalty for high crime.

The uncivilized savage, who may contemplate the death of another of his kind with equanimity, fights desperately to maintain his own life.

Down through all the scale of animate creatures the rage to stay alive manifests itself. "An animal's first impulse is self-preservation"—so Diogenes Laërtius remarked, or perhaps quoted from an earlier sage, some sixteen or seventeen hundred years ago, and self-preservation has never been refuted as the first law of nature. A parallel law of nature has been stated in lighter vein by numerous rhyming philosophers, not the least of them being Jonathan Swift, who wrote it thus:

> So, Nat'ralists observe, a Flea
> Hath smaller Fleas that on him prey;
> And these have smaller still to bite 'em,
> And so proceed *ad infinitum*.

Nature's law, though, lies not in that descending scale of size, but in the fact itself. When the big ones eat the little ones, they employ force; when the little ones eat the bigger, they employ guile or some equivalent. The law of self-preservation compels each living being, unless its sustenance be strictly vegetarian, to devour some other creature.

Man, who chooses to regard himself as the summit of creation, looks upon all inferior life as subject to his needs and pleasures. Without qualms he expects the lives of millions of cattle, sheep, swine, and poultry to be terminated in their prime in order that their proteins and fats may satisfy his hunger and delight his palate. Only lately has he taken the trouble to demand by law that their slaughter be conducted humanely.

Then we have that curious Neanderthal outcrop, the

"sport" hunter who shoots down the migrant ducks and geese, happily kills rabbits or lions, and blasts at squirrels, quail, and pheasants. When charged with evil he lamely explains that if he does not harvest the quail and deer they will become too numerous for their own good and die anyway. Who harvested them before gunpowder he does not say; nor does he identify the surreptitious gunner who took the eagle out of the treetop and the whooping crane out of the sky.

Mice, rabbits, hamsters, guinea pigs, rats, and other animals by hundreds of thousands are subjected to experimental diets and infected with diseases in the course of medical research. Man uses them to preserve himself, and to learn how better to care for the livestock he intends to eat.

With the laudable intent to keep people in better health, and in order to enhance our food supplies in quality and quantity and to protect them from injury and contamination, and in order to save some of our trees—for these purposes science has brought into being a remarkable group of instruments, mostly of chemical origin, called pesticides.

A 'cide is a killer, a destroyer. Homicide is murder of man. Suicide is self-destruction. Pesticide is a broad term that includes killers of whatever man considers pestiferous, dangerous to his life, his health, his food, his comfort—the insects, destructive rodents, weeds, plant diseases, fungi, bacteria. One might call a fly swatter a pesticide, or a rat trap; or a cat that catches rats, or the bird that feeds on injurious insects and gathers quantities of them for its young.

The chemical pesticides are, in varying degrees, poisons. That is why they are lethal to the pests against which they are used.

Like other instruments intended only for good purposes—automobiles, bathtubs, and electrical wiring, for examples—pesticides can be misused with deadly consequences, or used carelessly and unwisely in ways that in some instances have produced unintended and undesired effects. Out of these incidents have arisen fears and controversies. Where clear-cut facts have been disclosed, the elements of controversy have been or can be eliminated. Where facts are not known, or are misunderstood, controversies continue; and some continue because facts are ignored or because irrelevant facts are demanded.

A basic fact, certainly, is that pests constantly threaten destruction or diminishment to man's food supply, his health, comfort, some of his property and some desirable aspects of his environment: trees, for instance.

That pesticides do destroy pests and control them effectively, experience has proved beyond doubt. Millions live today because insecticides kill malaria mosquitoes. In the United States, pesticides have contributed abundantly to the plenitude and cleanliness of healthful foods.

We do have more to learn about these valuable weapons. Their use has been known to destroy robins and fish and other wildlife that we cherish. Through accidents and misuses some damage to humans has been done, and much more has been assumed.

After the basic fact about pesticides—their usefulness—some questions arise. The obvious one is how much, if any, sacrifice of nonhuman or environmental values should we make in order to protect the essential interests of human well-being.

Another question: Who shall decide? And who shall be trusted to enforce the decisions?

3/Alarms and Fears

THAT SOME DEGREE OF HAZARD ACCOMPANIES THE USE OF certain pesticides is a fact understood by all who are concerned, unless there be a few too ignorant to be aware of any kind of danger. That a degree of official regulation is essential and that appropriate precaution is necessary go without question.

Although the degree of hazard to human well-being is small, considerable fear has been fostered among those people who habitually approach with suspicion anything that is new, and among the nervous in whose minds alarm is easily aroused. No little of the still existing fear and alarm about pesticides stems from the famous book of 1962, *Silent Spring*.

The author of *Silent Spring*, Miss Rachel Carson, was a highly respected scientist in the field of marine biology. In addition she was a skilled writer. Two of her previous books, *The Sea Around Us* and *The Edge of the Sea,* had reached admiring audiences, the first having been a best seller. Both were in a field she had studied long and intimately and where her competence was unquestionable. The merit of those books assured for *Silent Spring* an eager readership, enlarged when a popular book club chose it for distribution. Regretted by her countless admirers, Miss Carson died from cancer in the spring of 1964. *Time* magazine (April 24, 1964) said of *Silent Spring*:

> To its author, it was more than a book; it became a crusade. And, despite her scientific training, she rejected facts that weakened her case, while using almost any material, regardless of authenticity, that seemed to support her thesis. Her critics, who included many eminent scientists, objected that the book's exaggerations and emotional tone played on the vague fears of city dwellers, the bulk of the U.S. population, who have little contact with uncontrolled nature and do not know how unpleasantly hostile it generally is.
>
> Nonetheless, *Silent Spring* was a runaway bestseller and an extremely effective polemic that stirred fierce argument, from village councils to the halls of Congress. Laws were proposed on local, state and federal levels to put rigid restrictions on the use of pesticides. Some of them were so sweeping that if they had been passed and enforced, they might well have caused serious harm. In advanced modern societies, agriculture and public health can no longer manage without chemical pesticides.

What might be termed an official estimate of *Silent Spring* appeared when the House of Representatives subcommittee on agricultural appropriations released its annual report in April, 1965. The subcommittee, of which the Hon. Jamie L. Whitten of Mississippi was chairman, had made a comprehensive study of pesticides in relation to human health, and of current pertinent activities by government agencies. After interviews with more than two hundred scientists and medical authorities, the report said of *Silent Spring*:

> The staff was advised, by scientists and by physicians, that the book is superficially scientific in that it marshals a number of accepted scientific facts. However,

> it is unscientific in (a) drawing incorrect conclusions
> from unrelated facts, and (b) making implications that
> are based on possibilities as yet unproved to be actual
> facts.

Numerous examples of "incorrect conclusions" are then cited.

The prime weakness of the book was that by innuendo and inference it suggested prospects of distress and disaster far beyond any probability.

How far beyond may be judged from a statement in the July 1962 *Journal* of the American Medical Association: "There is no confirmed record of a clinical effect from eating food treated with pesticides according to approved agricultural practice."

Dr. Wayland J. Hayes, Chief of the United States Public Health Service Toxicology Center, in the 1960 Annual Review of Entomology, *Pesticides in Relation to Public Health,* stated that "during the years of investigation it has been impossible to confirm the allegation that insecticides, when properly used, are the causes of any diseases either of men or animals. When misused, however," he adds, "they may produce poisoning."

Dr. Frederick J. Stare, chairman of the Department of Nutrition, Harvard School of Public Health, says: "As a physician and student of nutrition for the last twenty-five years, let me state categorically that I do not know nor have I ever heard of one single case of ill health in man shown to be due to adding approved chemicals to foods. And I say additional chemicals because I wish to emphasize that all foods are chemicals. You and I, too, are chemicals—so much water, protein, fat, carbohydrates, vitamins and minerals."

Human life seldom proceeds without encountering hazards and dangers of one degree or another. If one undertook to protect himself from every possible source of injury to his health or person, he would probably suffer more from his protective measures than from his external dangers. No one wants deliberately to take needless chances; even so, in the ordinary course of life fatalities overtake surprising numbers.

Year after year, for instance, about twenty thousand people die in the United States because of falls. Seldom are these falls of mountain climbers or from jobs on high buildings—they are falls in bathtubs, on stairs, on sidewalks, or equally commonplace and undramatic situations.

Twice as many die in automobile accidents—about forty thousand every year, more than one hundred every day. How many of these deaths take place because of the faults of others or from the errors of the victims we do not know. Nevertheless we do not outlaw automobiles nor hesitate to make use of them.

About seventy-five hundred die in the Unites States each year from burns, but fire continues to be permitted. Around sixty-five hundred die from drowning, but swimming has not been generally prohibited. Railroad mishaps account for around twenty-two hundred deaths a year, and firearms for nearly as many.

The lethal and social effects that the misuse of alcohol produces have been abundantly publicized. We are said to have some five million alcoholics, and that $422 million in wages are lost, with a cost of two billion annually to industry, because of drinking; yet various forms of alcohol remain popular.

The injuries, impairments, and disabilities from each of these causes far exceed all the fatalities that can in any way be traced to pesticides. Deaths have occurred from misuse of pesticides, and accidental deaths have resulted while handling ingredients. These have been rare and have grown fewer; the great efforts to insure that proper precautions always be taken have had their effects.

If the growing pesticide uses involved serious potential dangers, and if these were unavoidable, a better case against them might be made. On the other hand, if the advantages and gains are overwhelmingly great compared with the hazards to life, health, or comfort, few would hesitate to welcome their development or to utilize their advantages, any more than one refuses to drive his automobile today because it is dangerous. While recognizing and accepting the fact that life is constantly subject to numerous possibilities for bodily injury, contraction of disease, or termination, no one wants to add needlessly to the risks. In the light of all the facts about pesticides, the balance overwhelmingly favors the chemical and other weapons science has provided.

Dr. Edward F. Knipling, head of the Entomology Division, Agricultural Research Service, U.S. Department of Agriculture, is a leader in efforts to develop and improve nonchemical insect controls; more will be said about him and his work later. He has stated, "To my knowledge not one death (excluding accidental deaths) or serious illness has been caused among the people exposed to the insecticide (DDT) in connection with the control of insects . . . I estimate that no less than five million lives have been saved; no less than one hundred million serious illnesses have been prevented, through the use of DDT for controlling malaria, typhus, dysentery, and many other diseases."

If alarmists have spread the impression that the entire American landscape is being doused with insecticides, those who are worried may take comfort. More than 95 per cent of the nation's land receives no insecticidal treatment whatever, and only about 15 per cent of the land on which crops are grown undergoes insecticidal applications. Cotton, fruits, and vegetables are the crops most in need of chemical protection, though most others, also, require it when insect raids become critical.

One might suppose, from the furor of apprehension excited in recent years, that insecticides are something new; new, or at least the products of World War Two and after.

This, of course, is not the case. Nearly a century ago arsenic trioxide and acetate of copper were combined to make Paris green, a poison that, deadly to the potato beetle, saved the potato crop and protected others. A Frenchman in 1882 spattered some whitish stuff over his grapevines along the roadside and put up a poison sign to deter passing human marauders, only to find that he had discovered Bordeaux mixture, a combination of copper sulphate, lime and water. For several decades it served as the most widely used and effective spray against insect damages to fruits.

Other inorganic materials have been weapons against pests for a long time. Among them are arsenate of lead, calcium arsenate, zinc phosphide, sodium fluoroacetate, thallium sulphate, and compounds utilizing chlorine and fluorine.

Natural vegetable compounds hold a considerable place in the past and present history of insecticides. Strychnine, pyrethrum, nicotine, and rotenone are examples. The foremost rat poison for years was red squill, the product of a Mediterranean bulb; it was largely superseded by an anticoagulant substance first isolated from sweet clover, with which other effective compounds are now competing. Among other organic compounds are products known as organic mercurials, carbamates, dinitrophenols, and organic sulphur compounds.

In another category are malathion, parathion, TEPP (tetraethyl pyrophosphate) and phosdrin. Made up of oxygen, phosphorus, carbon, and hydrogen, these are known as organic phosphorus compounds.

Because of their versatile and selective effectiveness, by far the most widely used are the pesticides known as chlorinated hydrocarbons, so called because the ingredients involve hydrogen and carbon.

This group does not decompose so rapidly as the organic phosphorus compounds. For that reason it has been the prime target of the pesticide critics; it has excited most of the alarm that has been heard while, at the same time, it has accomplished untold good. DDT is the best known. Others in the group are chlordane, heptachlor, lindane, methoxychlor, toxaphene, aldrin, endrin and dieldrin. Such herbicides as 2,4-D and 2,4,5-T also are chlorinated hydrocarbons.

New names will continue to appear as science advances in its efforts to discover better means to subdue the pests that contend with man for the property he considers his by right of production or purchase. One should never forget that science of any kind, and particularly chemistry, does not remain static. Thousands of men and women in hundreds of laboratories patiently screen the facts of nature in a relentless and endless search for beneficial knowledge.

The facts of nature presented a problem—the fire ant—in the South a few years ago. This insect, an import from South America, had made itself a nuisance across several of the Gulf States. Its bite was painful: it annoyed livestock, and men sometimes refused to work where it was numerous. The mounds it built were bothersome in cultivated fields. Farmers presented the problem to Congress, which directed the Department of Agriculture to undertake a riddance program. The first attempt, utilizing the best knowledge at the time (1957), applied two pounds of heptachlor per acre. Besides killing fire ants, the treatment also killed some birds and wild animals. With smaller dosage and different application methods, this unhappy side effect was greatly reduced. Then, in 1961, a new insecticide, Mirex, became available from an industrial laboratory. Now a mixture is used that includes soybean oil to attract the fire ants and ground corncob grits as a carrier. This, with no more than one-seventh of an ounce of Mirex in five pounds of bait mix to the acre, brings the ant under effective control. No residue appears in milk, meat or crops, and neither wildlife, fish, bees, nor domestic animals show any ill effects.

The consumer who suffers uneasiness from fear that toxic residues from pesticides may contaminate his dinner might soothe himself if he knew all the precautions regularly taken for his protection. Briefly, the manufacturer who proposes to offer a new chemical that may be used in connection with foods must provide the Food and Drug Administration with voluminous data regarding the chemistry, toxicity, and residues of the product. The information must include facts— determined not by the manufacturer alone but by recognized, independent testing laboratories—about any effects on highly sensitive test animals. The FDA, then, if it approves the product, will set a tolerance level; the general rule is that this will be set at 1/100 of the lowest level at which effect on animals can be discerned. This is comparable, to use a far-fetched illustration, to proving that one hundred miles an hour is a safe automobile speed and having the officials, therefore, say that the legal and tolerable speed is one mile per hour. Moreover, the arrangements for enforcement of such safety precautions are excellent.

The farmers and others who use chemical pesticides have a built-in restraint: the materials are expensive. To apply greater amounts than the labels say are adequate would be throwing money away, which is considered poor business. Moreover, there is the risk of losing a crop, as happened some years ago when cranberry growers lost a large part of their year's market because a small amount of allegedly contaminated fruit was confiscated and publicized.

Although a higher rate of tolerance might be perfectly safe so far as consumers are concerned, each tolerance is set as low as possible consistent with effective use of the pesticide.

The analytical procedures themselves are carried to startlingly fine points. Legal requirements demand that tests to determine residues be measured in fractions of parts per million (ppm). A chemical man with a sense of humor—Louis A. McLean, Secretary of the Velsicol Chemical Corporation— offered an illustration:

"If a standard one-and-one-half-ounce jigger of vermouth is

added to the gin contained in a standard 8,000 gallon railroad tank car, not only is a very dry martini produced, but
the relationship of the vermouth to the gin is 1.46+ ppm."

Another measure: On lettuce the permitted DDT residue
tolerance is 7 ppm. One ounce of DDT residue on three tons
of lettuce would greatly exceed 7 ppm.

Now, however, new procedures have been developed, so
sensitive that they can detect chemicals in foods in parts per
trillion.

Dr. L.H. Haller, now retired from the Agricultural Research Service, has remarked that before a chemical is approved to control insects in food or animal feed, it "must pass
more rigid screening and review by competent pharmacologists, toxicologists, and other scientists than any other chemicals in use." He adds, "Scientists now know far more about
most commonly used insecticides than they do about most
of the chemicals that occur normally in foods."

Human carelessness leads to most of the deaths that are
recorded as accidental. In the bloody highway record, in
"mishaps" in homes and on the farm, the failure of some
person to observe due and sensible care can usually be traced.
Considering the large volumes of insecticidal materials made,
mixed, and used each year, the accidental deaths due to them
have been remarkably few. Dr. Wayland J. Hayes, Jr., of the
U.S. Public Health Service, is known as the nation's top medical authority on poisons. In a paper published in 1961 he
referred to a special study of accidental poisonings in 1956.
In that year 152 accidental deaths were attributed to pesticides. Of these, 104 were caused by materials in use before
1942 when DDT, the first of the chlorinated hydrocarbons,
was introduced. Of the total number, 94 were children under
ten, and 78 (more than half) were children under four.

Thousands of people each year handle pesticides in the
course of their occupations. Workers in the industries manufacturing and formulating the products, pilots who apply

crop dusts and sprays from the air and their helpers, commercial pest-control operators, and farmers, all come into close working contact with such materials.

Accidents do happen with carelessness or misuse, but the total is surprisingly small. Aspirin and related products produce a nearly equal death total and there again most of the victims are small children whose security in such matters is difficult to guard.

Read the label! This slogan goes wherever pesticides are used. Each pesticide has its purpose and each has its characteristics. So far as human life and health are concerned, little misgiving need be entertained if the sprays and dusts and mists are applied as the ever-present instructions direct. Never before, during all of man's hundreds of centuries on earth, has the prospect been so good for freedom from the disease, annoyance and economic loss which the insect species have the capacity to inflict. As sane and sensible people, we now know that the proper use of our newly available weapons can put us a few steps ahead of our arthropod adversaries.

4/The World's Hungry People

A PICTURE OF A HUNGRY CHILD, SICK FROM MALNUTRITION, staring hopelessly toward a troubled future, strikes to the heart of any normal person. To envision the full consequences of that little one's hunger arouses more than mere sympathy, more than simple sorrow that any child must go hungry.

One thinks of the little Americans he knows, cared for tenderly from the moment of birth, regularly fed according to the best knowledge of science, guarded with the highest pediatric skill, given every aid that parental love can muster. Here we aim that our children shall grow to adulthood physically strong and well. With strong and healthy bodies they will have opportunities to develop their other capacities without limit.

Put aside for a moment the heart-tugs that the picture of the hungry and ill-nourished child elicits. In terms of cold practicality, what is his future? And what does *his* future mean to our own children and grandchildren?

He may not have a future, for throughout his growing years he will be threatened by the diseases, many of them insect-borne, that are prevalent in his area. If he does achieve adulthood he will not likely ever be able to exert the physical energy that is required by what in this country we think of as an honest day's work.

Life expectancy in his country is probably no more than half the seventy years that the American child may anticipate. So his earning career may not be long. He will have neither strength nor years to do much for himself, his family, or his country. He may become one of the millions who never, throughout their lives, know what it is like to eat what the Western world generally considers three square meals a day.

Whatever his inclinations or special abilities may be, his best means of livelihood will likely be to till the soil. With primitive tools he will try to scratch out enough to sustain his family. The family probably will be large, because in his hand-labor economy every worker, young or old, can be an asset.

He will know, because communications have so shrunk the world, that elsewhere on his earth there are people who do not go hungry, and whose children can grow up full of health and vigor.

He will resent his condition. He will wonder why fate has dealt with him so badly. When the demagogues come, as they will, he will hear their words. Being ignorant, he may believe. Millions like him will believe—believe the wrong things, things that are not true. They will learn to hate those who wish to and can help them most.

And so the world of tomorrow, like that of today, will be a disturbed and turbulent planet. Our children and grandchildren will inherit our dreams of peace in their times, but they will still be only dreams.

So, when we examine the prospect that food may in time become plentiful for all children and all people everywhere, let's be realistic. Maybe it *can* become plentiful. While food alone will not guarantee a peaceful world, it is a long step worth trying for. No doubt always wrong-headed leaders will arise. We have seen well-fed wars in our time. But, like the house divided, a world half-hungry and half with plenty—in these times—will not stand unshaken.

Aldous Huxley, in a 1963 Ford Foundation paper, said:

> By shifting our attention from the now completely irrelevant and anachronistic politics of nationalism and military power to the problems of the human species . . . we shall be . . . reducing the threat of sudden destruction by scientific war and at the same time reducing the threat of more gradual biological disaster.

Few statesmen in these turbulent times appear to realize that the primary problem of the human species is agricultural. With rare exceptions their utterances tend to emphasize the political, diplomatic and military matters, none of which seem important to underfed masses of people.

Perhaps the statesmen cannot be too much blamed. In most countries the holders of high office can boast little or no actual experience with the land or, for that matter, with lack of food. Their predecessors worried even less about other people's hunger.

Even in the nineteenth century, other people's misery was easily borne by the fortunate. When he was asked about England's factory children, Lord Melbourne's exclamation was typical: "Oh, if you'd only have the goodness to let them alone!"

This second half of the twentieth century differs from the past, differs enormously. The poorest villagers in India, the most primitive tribesmen in Africa, are learning that millions of other people do not suffer with empty bellies. If they do not know, there are leaders who do know, and will tell them so. Food shortage becomes an internal and an international political problem.

Yet we have seen food-deficit countries proudly build steel

mills; sixty nations now have steel plants, where thirty years ago only half as many did. We have seen them erect high dams. They look forward to industrial development from the newly generated power. If the dams permit irrigation of arid acres, and farmers learn how to cultivate irrigated land, that will be good. Little other genuine progress is possible until a nation can be well nourished. The ill-fed worker lacks energy and thus produces little. Unless physical and mental energy propel him he is unlikely to be able to apply the intelligence he possesses, however great. The malnourished child never acquires that energy.

The nation that advances in agriculture until it can feed its people well has then prepared itself for the next step. In a progressive agriculture, fewer workers are required in the fields. If 90 per cent of the working force must be employed at growing food, little industrial production can be supported. But if only 80 per cent are needed for the farming, a few can be released to work in factories, or to become teachers and doctors. As that percentage declines, still more can employ themselves in activities that tend to raise the national standards of living. Even when special industrial or agricultural products can be exchanged outside the country, for foodstuffs or manufactures, the internal effects are similar. The wealth and power of the United States rest on the fact that only 7 per cent of the workers can feed abundantly the others, who produce riches in other forms. In contrast, the world over, about 55 per cent of all workers must be farmers.

Obviously the food-deficit countries, where every pound of food can become a tangible national asset, can ill afford to support an abundance of food-consuming pests.

If pests cost the United States $17 billion a year, as estimates indicate that they do, what can the underdeveloped world afford? That figure is huge even for a nation advanced agriculturally, where knowledge of how to fight pests is widespread and where nearly a billion is spent yearly upon control measures. In underdeveloped countries, insects and other pests are equally or more prevalent, knowledge of control measures is scanty, and means to use them are absent or far less adequate.

Tremendous strides have been taken to eliminate insect hazards to life and health in most of the underdeveloped countries—strides far ahead of those made toward improving the food supply. The reduction in malaria, dysentery and other plagues has sharply lessened infant mortality and measurably, in some places dramatically, extended life expectancy. Life is precious, and no one would have this progress reversed.

The consequence, though, is plain. When lives become longer, the population grows faster. More stomachs clamor for food. But while lives are being saved the accompanying steps toward enough food for more hungry people have been too short. So malnutrition tends to keep pace.

No one wants to argue that the eradication of pests can provide the whole answer to the world's hunger. Other serious barriers to a universal plenty, not germane to the present theme, add to the challenge. But no practical measure should be disregarded when the means for its accomplishment are at hand.

Unless all students of food and population relationships err badly, at least half of all human beings now on earth either get too little to eat, or exist on diets that are unsuitable for health and strength. Some authorities place the ratio of undernourishment and malnutrition even higher. How can this unhappy and dangerous condition be corrected? And how soon? What is the prospect for 1980, fifteen years from now? Or for 2000, only thirty-five years hence? Could it become worse instead of better?

It could grow worse, for three stubborn reasons.

(1) Farmers in the underdeveloped and food-short countries change their ways reluctantly.

(2) Population rises faster in the less fortunate countries than in those that are highly developed.

(3) The proportion of new land that may be brought into cultivation falls far short of matching the almost certain population growth.

To the first point little needs to be added. Ancestral farm ways are familiar. The inclination to take chances with new and unfamiliar recommendations is slight; the resistance is strong. Even in the United States "book farmin'" was scorned until, through 4-H Clubs and other mind-opening agencies, the way was cleared for the technological explosion that has so greatly advanced production in recent decades. Only as new generations learn to accept new ideas will old methods give way to better ones. The emphasis in agricultural education should be with youth.

Because fewer now die as babies and the adults live longer, population in underdeveloped areas rises as much as 2.5 per cent a year. This is three times the rate of increase in leading European nations and substantially larger than that of the United States in the 1950's. Our rate then was 1.7 per cent, and we called it a population explosion. In 1960 about a fifth more people occupied the world than ten years earlier. Now more than three and a quarter billion human beings inhabit the earth; by the end of this century the number is predicted to reach six billion.

If nearly four billion people cannot now obtain three nourishing daily meals, what are the prospects for feeding two billion more?

The situation is not necessarily hopeless, but it is precarious. Not quite all the arable land has yet been placed under cultivation or put to its best use for grazing. Considerable areas are available for producing more food. Not all of these are located where the hungriest people are going to be, though perhaps some migrations might be arranged. New lands in general will not be cultivated until capital, which the hungry do not possess, can be invested in the essential machinery and transportation facilities. Capital is not now much attracted to such pioneering.

With better methods, more irrigation where practicable, and more capital, most currently cultivated lands could be made to yield more.

To be realistic, however, one must expect that numbers of people are going to be rising faster than the available food supplies will be increasing. This will be especially true in the areas of greatest need.

Education, more efficient equipment, improved varieties of crop and pasture plants, and better land use, are but a few of the steps that will have to be taken rapidly if the ominous specter of hunger does not loom higher in the years ahead than will the more agreeable spectacle of rising production.

Here and there enormous gains can be attained as insect controls become applicable. This is a route along which measurable and rapid progress can be attained. Let us consider just two situations.

Four million square miles across central Africa—more than a fourth of that fascinating and burgeoning continent—are infested with tsetse flies. They transmit a disease called nagana to cattle, horses, sheep, goats and hogs. An apparently well hog may die within twenty-four hours after infection. The insects come in some twenty species, all more or less the size of house flies; where they are prevalent they have made domestic livestock production unprofitable and almost impossible. In Nigeria, where careful studies have been made, it was found that nagana caused thirty out of every hundred cattle deaths.

The native game and other animals appear to be largely immune or resistant to the disease, although they carry the trypanosomes that the flies transmit to domestic animals and to human beings.

In man the disease is usually known as sleeping sickness and has long been one of the hazards of travel in the infested portions of the continent. Early in this century, when the infection first reached eastern central Africa where the people had built up no immunity, more than 200,000 deaths occurred.

Unlike most of the insect species, the female tsetse does not lay eggs. She gives birth to a living larva, one at a time, about two weeks or less apart. The larva is hidden in the ground, to emerge as a fly a few weeks later. Another peculiarity of the tsetse is that males as well as females are bloodsuckers and thus can spread disease. Except for mosquitoes, no other insects are considered to be more dangerous to human well-being.

Much of the affected African area is densely peopled. The available foodstuffs tend to be mostly starchy, low in dietary essentials. If the tsetse fly could be brought under control, and healthy livestock industries established, a vast change toward better living could take place, with more milk for the children and more protein for all the people.

From the western coasts of Africa's bulge to eastern Pakistan and from the Mediterranean down the east coast of Africa as far as lower Tanzania, the desert locust menaces the crops, orchards, and pastures that man has tended. Across more than nine million square miles, nearly one-eighth of the human race lives under this one insect's threat.

The pest is not new. Remember the Book of Exodus, Chapter Ten, verses fourteen and fifteen?

> And the locusts went up over all the land of Egypt, and rested in all the coasts of Egypt: very grievous were they; before them there were no such locusts as they, neither after them shall be such.
> For they covered the face of the whole earth, so that the land was darkened; and they did eat every herb of the land, and all the fruit of the trees which the

> hail had left: and there remained not any green thing
> in the trees, or in the herbs of the field, through all
> the land of Egypt.

Whether modern swarms are or are not worse, they can be bad enough. Just an average swarm is estimated at 700 million locusts per square mile and may cover one hundred square miles—thirty to forty thousand tons of grasshoppers that consume 3,000 tons of food daily and have few natural enemies. Much larger swarms have been recorded. They eat everything green, often leaving behind nothing but holes in the ground where plants have been.

The female desert locust lays her eggs in the ground, usually in sand well below the surface. When first hatched, the young are wingless. Nevertheless they eat, march, and begin the gregarious behavior that culminates in the huge swarms a month later as the wings appear.

Most of the countries subjected to the desolating visits of the locusts have joined in a cooperative effort, sponsored by agencies of the United Nations, to reduce the desert locust devastation. Watchers try to report the first emergence of a hatch, so that airplanes can fly in to dust the area with insecticides. An Anti-Locust Research Centre is maintained in London; it is hoped that enough knowledge about the pests can be collected to make more effective control measures possible.

The tsetse fly and the desert locust are but two of several thousand species of insects that serve to keep the hungry half of the world hungrier.

Again comes the great question. What will happen when, only a third of a century hence, less than half of an American lifetime, the world population reaches the predicted six billion? As of now, out of the present estimated three and one-fourth billion, only some 450 million living in about twenty countries enjoy a fairly satisfactory standard of living. If the six-billion prediction for the year 2000 is correct, according to United Nations forecasts 3,639 million will be in the Far East, 947 million in Europe including Russia, 592 million in Latin America, 421 million in Africa, 27 million in the Near East, 29 million in Oceania and 312 million in North America—a rather small percentage here!

To maintain such increases, authorities calculate that the world's food output should be doubled in the next fifteen years and trebled by the century's end.

Will bugs eat it—or people?

PART TWO:

Pests and Conquests

5/Shall We Exterminate Them All?

WHEN THE LIFE PROCESSES OF SO MANY INSECTS MAKE them inimical to human interests, and when so many are annoying to have around, why not launch a war to eradicate them all?

Impossible; but even if it could be done successfully, the consequences would be disastrous. We need insects, and need them for many useful purposes. And they help us in a hundred ways to make our world beautiful and interesting.

We can retrain people to make their livings in unaccustomed ways, but we can't retrain the birds of the wild. Insects, adult, young, and eggs, furnish the bread and butter for millions of our most agreeable bird neighbors. Who has not watched a wren rushing to her nestlings with a beak full of larvae? The flycatchers, swallows, and swifts live wholly on flying insects. The handsome, many-colored little warblers and vireos feed on little or nothing else than insect forms. Robins and catbirds, thrushes, tanagers, kinglets, nuthatches, woodpeckers and many others select their proteins from the insect multitudes. Most of the seed eaters, quail, doves, sparrows, and finches, vary their diets with insect products. Some of the birds of prey and water birds include insects in their rations. If all the insect creatures were destroyed by one great aerosol bomb, starvation and distress would quickly beset the avian world.

Fish, too, are insectivorous, as anyone knows who has cast a fly for trout, or watched the finny species leap for a morsel of flying game. Aquatic insects are standard fish food. Many mammals—from the tiny underground vole to the giant ant-eater and the huge grizzly bear—support themselves wholly or in part from the abundant variety of the arthropod world.

If it were only because of the birds and animals we are fond of, that would be reason enough to refrain from indiscriminate war against insects. But the numerous other benefits man derives from insects pile the credits high on the bug ledger.

Dr. L.O. Howard, the eminent entomologist who did so much to arouse the justified hostility toward house flies and mosquitoes, wrote in *The Insect Menace* an opinion with which now, years later, most entomologists would substantially concur:

> I considered numerically 300 of the principal families of insects and concluded that of these families 116 were injurious to man, 113 were beneficial to man, and 71 contained both beneficial and injurious species, or species of undetermined economic status. It was rather a surprise to find that, of the 113 families comprising beneficial species, the insects of no less than 79 families prey upon other insects. A family is an immense group, comprising hundreds of genera and thousands of species; so that predatory and parasitic insects must be very abundant and must be an extremely important factor in the preservation of the so-called balance of nature. In fact, I am quite convinced that they are of far greater importance than the insectivorous birds and the other animals that destroy insects.

Almost anyone invited to name some beneficial insects would probably think of the honeybee; and after a little mental effort might also name the silkworm. Those two we would promptly exempt from destruction. The informed entomologist now, however, would probably be more emphatic than Dr. Howard. He would say that wholesale eradication of insects without regard to species or value would violently derange nature's and man's economy.

The economy would be deranged because the ecology would be upset. In a community from which insects were completely excluded the soil would fall static. No busy creatures would be burrowing into the ground to aerate it, to make little channels down which moisture can sink; no voracious jaws would forever be chewing up leaves and twigs, making them ready to be mingled with the sand and clay. The insect underground, while not in every instance benevolent, plays an important role in keeping the surface soil productive. Larvae of many kinds, ants, termites, mites, and the abundant, almost invisible springtails, hasten the decay of both vegetable and animal matter and aid its incorporation into the soil. One might easily spend a lifetime without ever having seen a springtail. Only a millimeter or so in length, they are so numerous that a single acre may contain several hundred thousand of them.

The predatory insects, which make their living by destroying other species, are mainly the friends of man. None, perhaps, is more conspicuous or better known than the handsome dragonfly, the colorful, gauze-winged speedster whose presence graces streams, ponds, swamps, and lakes. Devil's darning needle, he may be called, or mosquito hawk. His wingspread of four or five inches, the extraordinary rapidity of his flight, and sharp direction changes, draw the eye to him. His own head is practically all eyes, which have, it is said, as many as 20,000 sight units. He can see in all directions. When he pursues a mosquito, which with other small insects provide all his food, he scoops the victim into a sort of basket formed with his legs, then devours the creature without pausing in flight. The smaller, more delicate damselfly, related to the dragonfly, also eats mosquitoes and small, soft insects.

Friend to all gardeners and enemy to aphids, scale insects, mites, and caterpillar eggs are the aphis lions. These greedy larvae use long, sharp jaws to seize such garden pests; they drain the prey's interior, toss away the shell and go after another one. The adult form, called the lacewing, sports lovely wings and bright, striking golden eyes.

> *Lady bird! Lady bird! Fly away home!*
> *Your house is on fire, your children do roam!*

Everyone probably knows some of the neat, round-topped little lady beetles. The wing covers, reddish yellow with black spots or black with red spots, make them noticeable. No aphid, no scale or soft-bodied insect is safe from this voracious predator.

Operating a little differently than do the predators, the parasitic insects go about their regular business with no charitable intentions, yet even more than do the predators, they serve the interests of mankind.

Whoever has removed the nests that the mud dauber wasps attach to buildings has discovered that the nest was filled not with wasps but with spiders. The wasp captures the spider, stings him into immobility, lays an egg on him, and tucks him up into the mud nest. When the egg hatches into a larva it finds fresh spider meat ready at hand. This is the technique of the parasitic insects; they attach the eggs or young to a caterpillar, grasshopper, a worm or an adult host and doom that host to death as a convenient food for their offspring. Wasps and certain flies are among the most numerous of insects with this useful habit.

A southern countryman, particularly if he is old enough to remember the days when horses were everyday companions, might tell you about the wasp known as the "horse guard." Horses are distressed when any kind of insect hums near them. Botflies make them frantic. But when a big black and yellow horse-guard wasp comes buzzing and droning around, the horse shows no concern; perhaps if he could display pleasure he would do that. He knows that the wasp has come to catch flies. In the language of ecologists, the horse and the horse guard enjoy a mutually beneficial relationship. What the wasp does with the flies the horse may not know, except that after each visit there is one less fly. The wasps also frequent cattle and mules, obviously knowing that animals attract flies. Once she seizes a fly with her legs, the horse guard stings it to death and carries it to her nest. This she has constructed according to her own designs. For two or three days she digs in a sandy spot until she has made a tunnel a foot and a half long. In a little room at the end she lays one egg. Then she meticulously moves and spreads the sand from the heap she made at the entrance until no sign of a nest remains. Within a couple of days after the egg hatches, she starts bringing in flies, each time scraping away enough sand to enter the tunnel, and after each exit hiding it again with scrupulous care. The larva will consume fifty flies or more in two weeks. The horse guard usually has other nests at the same time, so her summers are busy.

One kind of wasp, when seen at all, is fascinating to watch. On an August afternoon several years ago cicadas were shrill-splitting the sultry air. Working over a lapful of manuscript, I sat in the shade of a big elm. When a soft thump nearby caught my attention, I saw a huge wasp disappearing under a grass clump. After a few minutes it came again into sight. Before it took flight I could see that the black-and-gold creature was at least more than half the size of my thumb. Not being an entomologist, I made a mental note to learn something about this outsize wasp. Shortly the shrill of a cicada in the next tree stopped abruptly, in the middle of a sentence, so to speak. Minutes later the wasp again zoomed down to the grass clump. It was carrying a cicada, apparently paralyzed because it showed no struggle.

During the afternoon I noticed this or a companion wasp slowly tugging another cicada up a tree trunk. A reference book filled out the story. The wasp captures and immobilizes the cicada, but it is too big for her to manage in flight. So she walks with her victim up a tree to a point where she is high enough to volplane down to the opening of the nest burrow. That is usually hidden, as this one was, under a grass clump. Inside, she deposits an egg on the cicada, confident from the ancient experience of her race that another generation of her kind will one day find a ready-to-eat cicada.

Accounts of entomologists' importing foreign predatory and parasitic insects to stop the ravages of injurious alien bugs that have invaded America appear in Chapter Eighteen. Here is an even stranger tale of how an insect from the southern hemisphere was induced to reverse his winter and summer, and then to destroy an unwelcome, poisonous alien plant.

The weed came from Europe. It traveled not only to the United States, but to Canada, New Zealand, and Australia. Traditionally in Europe it blooms on June 24, the day of St. John the Baptist, and so over there it is called St.-John's-wort. As long ago as the beginning of this century it was noticed in northern California near the Klamath River, and hence is sometimes called Klamath weed.

Klamath weed became highly unwelcome in the range country as soon as its nature was known. It is poisonous. The mouths of cattle and sheep that eat it become sore. They may blister, and animals become angry and hard to handle. They grow scabby, and they fail to thrive. The weed does not kill them. But as it spread over several hundred thousand acres of once-good native pastures in Oregon, Idaho, Montana, Washington, and Nevada, it loomed up as the only green growth after the early-season grasses dried up. It crowded out the native plants. The infested areas were unsafe to use.

Australia had managed to naturalize leaf-feeding beetles that ate the weed in Europe. U.S. entomologists brought two of the species from Australia to California. There, after deceiving the adults a little by sprinkling them daily to make them believe the rainy weather season had come, they led the bugs to make themselves at home. Within three or four years the beetles, which eat practically nothing else, had so reduced the Klamath weeds that the native plants were reappearing and the pastures were again becoming productive rather than poisonous. Now that the imported insects have made themselves at home, the objectionable weed will no longer dominate the area it had taken over.

Although vast sums must be spent to destroy noxious and undesirable insects, and enormous care must be taken to prevent new and unwelcome kinds from entering the country, other foreign as well as native species do have high economic value.

An Australian experience proved the value of another insect for dealing with an introduced plant pest. The scale insect which, in India, produces lac, formerly the principal source of shellac, is well known. From the dried and ground-up bodies of a related insect the once highly prized red cochineal dye is made. The dye still finds uses in cosmetics, beverages, and as a culinary decoration. A pound of dye requires some 70,000 of the insects.

The cochineal lives on cactus. Back in 1787 a gentleman imported cactus plants to Australia, hoping to develop a dye industry there by using the cactus as his bug pasture. While his plans did not succeed, the cactus did. Millions of acres became so densely grown with prickly pear that they killed out the native plants and destroyed the land's value. Between 1920 and 1937 Australia imported around fifty different kinds of insects before finding a moth from Argentina that cleared out the cactus stands and made room for grass to grow again.

Considering the livelihood it has furnished to millions of

people for three or four thousand years, the silkworm deserves to be mentioned in even a brief account of beneficial insects. For two thousand years or more the Chinese kept this benefactor as a national secret and made any attempt to carry it out of the country a capital offense. Someone did it, though, about 555 A.D. Mainly because of labor cost, the several efforts to establish a silk industry in the United States have failed. Silk remains a product of the Orient and of some Mediterranean countries. Here the synthetic "nylon worm" has largely taken over the market.

Of all the services that insects perform for themselves but to the advantage of people, none is quite so important nor would seem more pleasant than that of visiting flowers.

In the wild, there are countless trees, shrubs, and wild flowers that depend for their ability to produce seeds upon the insects which pollenize them. Bees, wasps, flies, gnats, beetles, moths, and butterflies, all function as agents in the processes of plant reproduction. At least fifty domestic crops produce fruit or seed largely because honeybees seek nectar from their blossoms and distribute their pollen. Bumblebees have been recognized at least since Darwin's time as important to the seed setting of red clover. Wild bees, of which North America is estimated to have probably 5,000 species, vie with the honeybee in the pollination business. A hundred or more wild bee species are known to visit alfalfa.

The honeybee can boast a lengthy American lineage, although it is not indigenous. The first ones did not make it in on the *Mayflower*, but they were brought soon afterward. The colonists wanted the honey.

Nowadays, when the beekeeper sells the honey from his hives he recovers only a portion of what the bees have contributed to the national economy. The bees do make some two-hundred million pounds of honey a year, and four million pounds of wax, which their keepers can sell. In the process the bees improve the yields for growers of half a hundred different fruit and seed crops—a benefit worth far more than the honey.

Most apples, plums, sweet cherries, onions, red and white clovers would fail to produce fruit or seed without the aid of bees or other insects to pollinate their blossoms. Beekeepers rent their colonies to farmers who need them, often moving them five hundred or a thousand miles for that purpose. Thus some northern bees spend their winters in Florida.

If this were simply a treatise on the lives of insects, rather than an effort to present a rational view of their relationships to human interests and of what man does about them, accounts of how insects do favors for the human race could readily be multiplied. Within this brief chapter, the intent has been simply to point out that, despite the assassins, troublemakers, and thieves in the six-legged world, large numbers are highly valuable neighbors. Not a few have esthetic qualities that add something to our scenery. Others live in ways that, from our human viewpoint, mingle vices and virtues.

Certainly if disaster struck the springtails, the honeybees, the aphis lions, the dragonflies, and countless others, a great deal, perhaps much more than anyone now knows, would be subtracted from our human environment. While our efforts to live in health, abundance and comfort demand that the vile ones be kept in check, and sometimes annihilated, we shall in general do well to watch which direction the spray nozzles point.

Now, let's search for some of the sinners.

6/Frail Assassins

THROUGH ALL THE AGES, INSECT-BORNE DISEASES KILLED more people than all the wars recorded and forgotten. By weakening the living, they have cancelled out enough human energy to have made all mankind rich.

The two diseases that are said to have caused, directly and indirectly, nearly half of all human deaths, are scourges that one kind of insect spreads: malaria and yellow fever. The murderous bearer of these often fatal maladies is that frail and delicate little assassin, the mosquito.

. . . One day the word reaches you that malaria has put your vigorous young man into a hospital. Malaria? You hurry to an encyclopedia. You get the friendly family doctor aside to probe his knowledge. It may not be so bad; it might be awful. The overseas messages, usually delayed, are reassuring, but no more than just that.

Years later, after he comes home, you manage to piece out the story. The little you had learned was only part of it. You hear about a hot evening on the Nigerian coast; he was fully clad in uniform, mosquito boots, and protective head-dress, as darkness descended over the out-of-door assignment.

No mosquito repellent had been available. The backs of his neck and hands were exposed.

Then, a few days later, came the attack. One memory seems to survive from a Royal Air Force Hospital: being awakened from a stupor while two doctors and two nurses struggled to comfort the sweat-soaked patient and change the bed linen.

Recovery! Comforting news slowly crosses the sea. Then, eight months later, the first recurrence, in a healthful area two thousand miles farther away in the southern hemisphere—a strike so sudden and so weakening that the young officer could only remember that it took three hours to struggle ten feet across the floor, while recalling in fleeting moments of consciousness that he must somehow reach that telephone. Shattering chills alternated with high fevers. Recovery again, and in eight more months another bout for the third hospital sojourn. The swollen spleen could be felt as it pressed over the diaphragm.

Malaria has its varieties. This was the malignant tertian kind. Not for nine years did the occasional touches cease to strike, though no longer so severely. Of these one sharp memory was that of looking out a hotel window to see neon signs flashing, being able to note the colors but unable to read the letters. Unpleasant for one who knew about the potential permanent brain injury that a recurrence could still bring.

One mosquito!

More than two thousand species of this deadly devil encircle the earth. Not all of them, fortunately, are quite so corrupt.

By now the terrors of yellow fever are nearly forgotten. Boston once had a siege of it. In 1793 an epidemic drove the government of the United States out of Philadelphia. Friends passing in the streets barely nodded, and tried to keep to the windward from anyone who wore a mourning badge. The Gulf and Caribbean port cities for years lived in almost perpetual fear of so frightful an agent of sudden death. It had defeated the French effort to build a Panama Canal and was the horror of Havana in Spanish-American War times. The danger has faded now, but it is not yet extinguished. In tropical South American jungles it persists. Let some infected monkey be bitten by the right mosquito, and let that mosquito bite a man, and let the man be bitten by mosquitoes that have access to other human prey, and yellow jack will again make headlines.

The American today has small occasion to worry about catching one of the insect-borne killers that still threaten lives around much of the earth. In his sanitized home, where he bathes in and drinks water that is chlorinated, surrounds himself by electrical and chemical cleaning agents, has his windows screened and his pasteurized milk delivered at his doorstep, his concern over probable attack upon his family by bubonic plague, malaria, or typhus is justifiably slight. They are not now hazards in Ardmore or Evanston, Pasadena or Westchester. He has plenty of time to worry about the possibility that a couple of parts per million of DDT or some other pesticide may contaminate his food or remain to reside somewhere within his body. If he doesn't die in bed an automobile accident or a bathroom fall may be his primary hazard.

Yet his immunity to insect-borne sickness and death is not really complete. In Philadelphia suburbs on the New Jersey side of the Delaware River, during the last half of 1964 ninety-two cases were identified as St. Louis encephalitis and seven people died from it. Around Houston, Texas, where the 1964 outbreak was called the worst of the kind in United States history, encephalitis deaths reached thirty-two and 712 people were reported officially as suspected cases. More than two hundred people in the Tampa Bay area were infected in 1962. The vector? None other than Culex, the common house mosquito. Chickens, pheasants, and other fowl may be infected with the disease, yet not be harmed. Mosquitoes that bite them and then bite humans may transmit it; paralysis, mental retardation, or death may be the consequences.

How man achieved mastery over yellow fever and found how to prevent malaria are noble tales, now well enough known to need no elaboration here. Yellow fever retreated to the jungle after Walter Reed and his bold colleagues learned how to deal with *Aedes egyptii,* the mosquito that, like the housefly, prefers to live in the neighborhood of man. By keeping the old tin cans and tires empty, changing the water daily in the bird baths, keeping the rain barrels covered, and hitting the female mosquito with chemicals, the vector has been thinned out; few places to breed and no welcome anywhere. But people and municipalities do grow careless.

Malaria has by no means been so completely restricted. It continues to be one of the world's major diseases; though we think of it as a disease of the tropics, it may appear anywhere except near the poles. Archangel, in the high north of Soviet Russia, once had an outbreak, and Canada has not escaped. About half of the world's population lives in areas that have been subject to malaria. In January 1965, the World Health Organization announced its claim that 813 million people have been released from its threat after a decade-long campaign to eradicate the disease. Insecticides, screens, and drainage of Anopheles mosquito breeding places have been actors in the success so far. Yet, if the claim is correct, another fourth of the human race still needs to fear every mosquito bite.

Aedes egyptii, the same mosquito that carried yellow fever, also peddles dengue, or breakbone fever. Not fatal but productive of pain and debilitation, dengue can quickly become epidemic. In 1963 Puerto Rico experienced an outbreak that infected ten thousand people and set about new efforts to reduce the mosquito population. On Guam and other Pacific Islands it put considerable numbers of our World War Two troops into hospitals. Texas underwent a dengue epidemic in 1922 that recorded more than half a million cases.

The grisly details that would be essential to describe the progress of elephantiasis, a horrible malady that disfigures its pitiful tropical and subtropical victims, will not be described here. In human lymph glands the mosquito-communicated worm grows from minuteness to three or four inches in length; swellings distort the genitals and extremities. A similar mosquito-carried ailment is filariasis, frequent in tropical parts and once briefly found in the southeastern United States, prevention of which might do more for Egypt's people than the Aswan Dam will do.

This century's world war against mosquitoes deserves more historical notice than it has been accorded. Multivolume scientific works about the insect itself, its many species and varied behaviors, have been printed, but no one has fully narrated the valiant protective efforts man has organized here and abroad. New Jersey, once but no longer famed for the rapacity of its mosquitoes, organized a Mosquito Extermination Association in 1912, which with state and other support, continues to be unceasingly and efficiently active. Virginia, New York, California, Illinois, and Florida, and perhaps other states, have created mosquito abatement districts which marshal power shovels, aircraft, foggers, hydraulic spray equipment and amphibious vehicles in their attempts to control the pests. Some two hundred and fifty local, state and federal agencies work at the job. Diversity of attack has been necessary to battle a creature that breeds in quiet water whether it is clean, dirty, fresh, or salt, whether located in vast marshes, tin cans, holes in trees, or even in the spoonful of water the axil of a plant may collect. In Trinidad it does no good to fight malaria by spraying or drying up the ground puddles because the vector species there breeds only in the axils of certain air plants attached high up in the trees.

DDT and other insecticides have become decisive factors in the wars against malaria mosquitoes. Why this is so has been explained clearly in a brief statement by Dr. E. F. Knipling:

> A mosquito cannot transmit malaria until about two weeks after it has fed on a person having the disease. If the houses and other resting places of mosquitoes in the vicinity of human habitations are treated, the mosquitoes will be killed sometime during the two-week period. This break in the chain is the key to the success of DDT in control of malaria and other diseases transmitted by mosquitoes. It is sometimes difficult to realize how important this one development is to people everywhere, but the fact is that malaria and other important mosquito borne diseases cause more than 100 million cases of illness and many deaths each year.

Two able authorities joined to discuss "Carriers of Human Diseases" in the 1952 USDA Yearbook. They were F.C. Bishopp, who since 1909 had been investigating the topic, and Cornelius B. Philip, an authority on medical entomology with the U.S. Public Health Service, a student of the field in several parts of the world and a colonel in the U.S. Army Sanitary Corps during World War Two. They say: "Probably ten thousand kinds of mites, ticks and insects infect man directly or indirectly with disease. Most of them are only occasional and accidental carriers. Many spread diseases among livestock and wildlife and carry them from the animal reservoirs of infections back to persons."

Fortified by millennia of success, these ten thousand pests continue adamant in their ways, changing only to resist extinction; some have accomplished this by producing strains resistant to the insecticides that have killed fellows in their species. The housefly is one such. The resistance does not change their ancestral ways. Because these ways may prove fatal to man, make him sick, destroy his food, consume his property or annoy his comfort, the human alternatives are but two: avoid the bug or kill him.

Nearly every year medical science discovers that arthropods convey a disease for which causes previously have been uncertain. A few of the more serious sicknesses, fatal or nonfatal, definitely known to be borne to humans by insects, fleas, ticks, lice, or mites, are these: sleeping sickness, tularemia, dysentery, bubonic plague, typhus, murine typhus, scrub typhus, trachoma, yaws, trench fever, relapsing fever, Chagas' disease, Rocky Mountain fever and Q fever. A complete list would be far longer.

The *World Review of Pest Control,* autumn of 1962 issue, carried an article by A.W.A. Brown, professor of zoology in the University of Western Ontario. Professor Brown vividly recapitulated a few of the marvelous advances in human health produced by man's new weapons for controlling his ancient insect adversaries:

> Between 1945 and 1954 the death rate in underdeveloped countries decreased by 32 per cent, so that the world death rate fell to eighteen per thousand, a figure less than twice that in the developed countries of Europe and America; since 1947 the death rate in India has been halved. Only a small part of this phenomenon is due to improved nutrition, and a little more to improved housing. It is the incidence of insect-borne disease that has fallen so dramatically; while a small contributing cause is the substitution of tractors for farm animals, the main factor is the control of the insect vectors by synthetic insecticides.
>
> It is difficult to find figures to prove this point universally, but one instance is vivid enough: A program of spraying houses with DDT in Ceylon reduced the death rate by 34 per cent in a single year. It was for the outstanding contributions that DDT offered to

human health in the tropics that the Nobel Prize in medicine was awarded to Paul Muller in 1948.

DDT can be produced cheaply and it is easily formulated. Extremely stable and highly insecticidal, DDT produces deposits that remain lethal to insects which walk over or rub against them; thus it is the residual insecticide par excellence. Moreover, under normal conditions of use, DDT is harmless to man and his domestic animals.

This insecticide burst upon the world scene in late 1943 when the application of DDT dusts inside the clothing of the inhabitants of Naples completely stopped an outbreak of louse-borne typhus. Soon DDT sprays applied to walls of houses and farmyards were controlling houseflies with a thoroughness that had never been seen before. Its effectiveness against adult Anopheles mosquitoes was such that treatment of the inside walls of human dwellings with DDT deposits resulted in a striking decrease of new cases of malaria. Moreover, the flies, sand flies, bedbugs, and cockroaches disappeared from the sprayed houses and the occupants became well-rested as well as healthy. Dosages of DDT below one part per million controlled mosquito larvae breeding in still waters, and even lower doses were sufficient to eliminate black fly larvae from streams. Applied repeatedly to African vegetation, this insecticide could clear whole areas of tsetse fly.

To this excerpt we add three further sentences from Professor Brown:

"There are few problems in public health entomology that cannot be combatted with either DDT as the first-line weapon, BHC or dieldrin as the second-line, or finally with some organo-phosphorous compound."

"The use of DDT in virtually every part of the world has had no deleterious effects on the occupants of the sprayed houses, and there have been virtually no accidents among the 130 thousand spraymen now involved in the [WHO] campaign."

And finally:

"For those in doubt as to the usefulness of insecticides for human health and welfare, a night on the earth floor of any unsprayed African hut is suggested—if they can find one."

Our own houses are preferable. But are they completely bugless?

7/Lady, Beware!

SCREENS WE TAKE FOR GRANTED. FOR MOST OF THE YEAR they cover our windows and doors. Without them, the flies, wasps, mosquitoes, moths, bees, and other winged nuisances would move in. A lighted room at night would attract swarms.

Screens cost money, and the bother of putting them up, taking them down, storing and cleaning them, add to the exasperations of life. For an ordinary American home, one that has two doors and only a dozen windows, stock-size screens are likely to cost more than $100. For, say, forty million houses, that would put the screening cost above four billion dollars, just to keep the flying bugs from invading the living quarters.

Despite all the screens and barriers, creepers, crawlers and fliers find means to bring their unwelcome presence into even the best-kept homes. No woman ever brags about the insects in her house. For a bit of conversational material she may mention one as though it were a rare discovery. But she will prefer to deal with her insects in determined silence.

No insect carries the stigma of social disgrace so much as bedbugs. Though far from being extinct, progress has made them "no longer common in the United States," a USDA publication says, and then adds, "but they do occur—in the most luxurious residences as well as in modest homes." From bus, train, airplane, hotel, motel or theater, the bedbug may find his way to a new address; even, maybe, in a bundle of laundry.

A hungry bedbug goes out for blood, human blood. He can wait a year if he must to find it, but when he does he gorges until his quarter-inch body grows longer and turns from brown to dull red. The digested blood leaves spots on bed linen, mattresses, or wherever he goes to rest. Two undetected bedbugs will before long provide more, for the female finds places where the bed frames are joined, or around mattress tufts, that suit her well for laying eggs. Though innocent of transmitting disease until proved guilty, the bug had been suspected as a possible carrier of tularemia.

In bygone days, elimination of bedbugs from an infested home was a major housecleaning job. Even now strains seem to have developed that are resistant to DDT or lindane, but a thorough dousing of all bed parts and nearby areas, including upholstered furniture, with a recommended insecticide, will exterminate the pests. There is no other way to do it.

Perhaps because when seen at all his size makes him conspicuous, the filthy cockroach ranks high on the cleanly housewife's list of insect horrors. A close relative of the less-hated grasshoppers, the cockroach must be considered as being, from his standpoint, among the most successful of insects; he has persisted with little change from extremely ancient times. *La cucaracha,* as the Spanish peoples call him, may be viewed as a real cosmopolitan, at home in almost any except the coldest regions. Although one species would seem to be ample for all practical purposes, some twelve hundred species are know. Of these, five find such places as the American home, restaurant, food store, or saloon to be satisfactory places of abode. No matter how inhospitable the homekeeper wishes to be, the cockroach may move in from the house of a more tolerant or less careful neighbor, or may hide himself somewhere in the grocery bag.

In time of darkness he explores. About food he is not discriminating. Any kind of human provision will suit him, or if barred from something better he will nibble clothing, curtains, shoes, books, paper, or plain filth. He carries dirt from one object to another and, not being housebroken, discharges his feces wherever he goes. Normally he will soil or damage much more than he eats. His habits permit him to leave behind him the organisms of salmonellosis, responsible for many cases of food poisoning.

Any hiding place will suit him so long as it is dark and out of the way during daylight. Drainpipes, behind sinks, in furnace rooms, in cracks under the woodwork, he conceals his fetid self by day. The brown-banded roach often hides under tables or other furniture, in a bookcase, desk or television cabinet. While he and his females do not reproduce so rapidly as flies or plant aphids, the female for a time carries her sixteen eggs about, then puts them away in some crevice from which the young eventually emerge.

The American and oriental cockroaches may grow to a length of two inches. The German, brown-banded and Australian adults are about a half-inch long, and multiply more rapidly. Careful sanitary measures and a variety of insecticides can help to keep a home at least temporarily free from these unpleasant insects, although eternal vigilance is the only way to prevent their renewed appearance. Once established, nothing short of a thoroughgoing anti-insect onslaught will eliminate them.

Ants, like the cockroaches, come in several species, and are not much more popular as uninvited household guests. Also like cockroaches, they crawl over any food they can reach without regard to where their feet have been previously. Much as one is supposed to admire the ants' industry, it is

safer to restrict them to outdoor work. They will nest under
the flooring or under objects left on the floor, or in any such
place where they can hope to carry on their multiplication
unseen. Those that do nest outside are adept at finding a
small crack that permits them to explore inside. By closing all
such openings and treating their travel routes with suitable
insecticides they can be controlled, temporarily at least. But
their motto is, "We shall return!"

Clothes moths and carpet beetles cause damage to household goods of American families that is estimated at as much
at $500 million a year. The estimate will seem reasonable to
anyone who has seen a patch of expensive woolen carpet denuded of its pile, or a good wool suit punctured with all-too-
visible holes.

The clothes moth comes in two species and the carpet
beetle, often called buffalo moth, comes in four. The adults
themselves do little damage, but the females lay eggs and the
eggs hatch into voracious larvae. No more than a half-inch
long, only a quarter-inch if they are the mottled carpet beetles, these larvae are alike in their tastes. They chew up not
only rugs and clothing, but will go after draperies, uphol-
stery, hair mattresses, blankets, brushes, and pillows. Anything suits them that is wool, mohair, hair, bristles, down,
feathers, or fur. Lint and hair encourage the pests when allowed to gather in corners where the vacuum cleaner does
not always reach. The housewife's propensity to move the
furniture may have a better reason than she realizes: Places
under heavy furniture are especially suitable for insect head-
quarters; moving such pieces occasionally is a good protective
measure. Even when all the precautions are observed, the
moths and carpet beetles will occasionally appear. Then the
situation calls for vigorous insecticidal treatment.

While insects may not attack the china, metalware, brick,
or concrete around the home, little else is immune. The several species of powder-post beetles, for instance, specialize at

eating into furniture and into the wooden parts of the house. A really serious infestation may even weaken the structural framework. The larvae, seeking the cellulose or starch upon which they flourish, like joists, studs, rafters, or floors. What looks like a shothole in a piece of furniture is likely to be the exit from a tunnel within. A trace of woody powder offers a sure sign of their presence. The old house borer is found mostly in the East, but other powder-post beetles may be encountered anywhere. For a serious infestation of these destroyers a professional exterminator is needed.

Termites, as everyone knows, can practically eat up a house, and can easily damage sills and portions near the ground so badly as to require expensive replacement. Most common in the southern states, they may appear all over the United States except in Alaska. The subterranean variety nests in the ground and works from there into the nearest wood. The less common nonsubterranean variety forms colonies within the wood; it is not found in the North. The easiest way to distinguish a termite from an ant is to remember that ants are wasp-waisted and termites are not. Carpenter ants also eat out and nest in woodwork, but are seldom a serious pest. The best way to eliminate termites is to turn the job over to a professional, although their entrance to a building can be prevented by metal barriers or by poisoning a strip of soil; even these attempts are best made by someone with experience.

Silverfish and firebrats, a pair of twin nuisances, resemble each other in manners as well as in appearance. The firebrats prefer to hide themselves in the warmer parts of the house while silverfish like the cooler basement. Both will wander about at night, eating cereals, paper or paste if starchy, or chewing on starched or rayon fabrics, wallpaper and books.

Centipedes and millipedes normally live out of doors and, except for their unpleasant appearance, are not especially objectionable. A period of heavy rains or its opposite, extreme drouth, may prompt millipedes by thousands to move indoors. As is true with crickets, it takes a tight house to keep them out.

Ticks and mites are, strictly described, not insects. Along with spiders and scorpions, as well as the millipedes and centipedes, they are a separate branch of the ancient line of arthropods. The mites, which include chiggers, often ride into the house with rodents, accompany a person coming in from a poultry coop or pigeon loft, or enter with the aid of birds that nest in chimneys or near openings. The gentle, confiding phoebe who builds over a porch post often scatters mites when she flies off, especially by the time of her third brood. Pet birds, too, may carry mites. The annoyance may be perceptible but the actual damage from them is small. Fortunately the chiggers one gathers out of doors do not breed indoors. Ticks are not exclusively the property of the dog, but he will most likely account for their coming indoors to lay eggs, which hatch into more ticks.

Fleas would just as soon bite a human as the dog or cat. The eggs they lay on Fido or Puss may hatch in a chair or other favorite resting place for the pet. Some species are disease carriers. In a home that has been vacant during an extended period, fleas have been known to take over until returning human occupants have found the premises unlivable —after all, one flea bite continues to be noticeable for several days. Fortunately the pets' fleas can be handled by proper care, and a vigorous attack with suitable insecticides can clear up the house.

The spider is not an insect either, being an arachnid, but is no more welcome in the well-kept house because of that scientific distinction. The immaculate housekeeper will not tolerate their webs, even though she knows they may trap some other less respectable arthropod. Although many kinds of spiders choose human dwellings for their homes, only one is a really bad neighbor. That, of course, is the black widow, whose female is the lethal member of the species. Her bite can lead to death and demands the most immediate medical attention. The black widow is small, maybe a half-inch long, long-legged but roundish of body, shiny black, usually with a red, orange or brownish-yellow mark underneath. More common in the southern than in northern states, the black widow may be found in both; spots outside but near the house are more likely to harbor the creature than the living quarters.

Several varieties of wasps aspire to be considered household insects. They come in if they can. They do kill numbers of injurious insects and in that respect are considered to be beneficial. Nevertheless their stings are uncomfortable; for persons with certain allergies they can be serious, even fatal. For that reason the mud daubers, yellow jackets and paper-nest builders have to be sprayed or dusted out of business when they come too close to human pathways.

Ever meet up with a psocid? Or find insect life among the dry foods on the pantry shelves? "Pantry pests" is the acceptable name for all the moths, beetles, weevils, including the psocids, that mysteriously develop in the flour, meal, cereals, dried fruits, nuts, even in with the chili powder, red pepper and paprika. They also appear in spaghetti, macaroni, noodles, dog biscuit, bird seed, chocolate, dry soup mixes, and dehydrated foods. If before throwing out the infested foods anyone wants to identify the species, among those to look for will be the Indian meal moth, the rice weevil, the sawtoothed grain beetle, the cigarette beetle and the interestingly named "confused flour beetle."

One authority has remarked that if each family in the United States discarded a half dollar's worth of food each year because of the pantry pests, the total loss would exceed $20 million. The little things can make their ways into any container that is not closed perfectly tight, and can maintain reserves of their species in any bits and particles of food that has been spilled on the shelves. The only preventive that works is thorough cleanliness of shelves and the right amount of the proper spray before packages are replaced. A half hour of 140-degree oven heat will sterilize suspected food.

A psocid, incidentally, is a tiny, soft-bodied wingless insect that joins the other dry food nuisances; it is also called a book louse.

The foulest, dirtiest and generally most dangerous of all the insects frequenting the house was once, and may still be, the most abundant. That is the housefly. The housefly hatches from the filthiest of garbage and manure, and flies with ease to the kitchen or wherever it can find food to contaminate. It has been known to spread typhoid, dysentery, and infant summer complaint.

When the DDT types of insecticides came into use, there was hope that the housefly might cease to be a pest. Though billions of flies did succumb, the species managed rather promptly to breed new strains that refused to be killed by such chemicals. However, since communities and householders take more care to prevent the accumulation of fly-hatching refuses, municipalities demand sanitary standards, houses are better screened, and since the sprays still eliminate many, the housefly has become less of a pest.

The annoying little fruit flies soon disappear when no fermenting vegetable material is permitted to attract them. Besides the housefly and fruit fly about a dozen other similar species visit homes. Among them are the cluster fly, the biting housefly, the little housefly, stable fly, cheese fly, bluebottle fly, blowfly, flesh fly, dungfly, moth fly, humpback fly and window fly. All these are objectionable but fortunately not so numerous.

In the tropics and in those parts of the world where poor housing prevails, household insects become far more pestiferous than in most of the United States. In an unscreened mansion in the South American tropics a few years ago the writer met more flies during two hours around the kitchen and dining room than he has seen in ten years at home.

This chapter opened with what must be a conservative estimate as to what insects cost this country's householders in terms of screen protection alone.

One wonders about another cost. How many hours a week, month, or year does the housewife work to prevent insects from invading her home, damaging its contents, or annoying the occupants? If these hours were all paid for at prevailing maids' wages, the national total would surely rise into the multimillions. Without the handy household insecticides, it would be far more.

8/A Grass Roots Poll

WHETHER THE SUBURBAN HOUSE SITS IN THE MIDST OF A small lot or is surrounded by a more spacious spread, it offers large opportunities for the student entomologist. He can be fairly sedentary if he elects to be a bug watcher. He will not have to expend energy at going far afield: he can build a lengthy list or accumulate an impressive collection from within his own boundaries.

The lawn is usually the property owner's pride. The lawn will probably include at least two dozen types of entomological specimens and a few separate species of each, all grimly determined that his grass will provide sustenance for them and for their sometimes abundant descendants.

Reasonably early in the spring, when his ambitions, energies, and determination are likely to be at the peak, he might start out with a sharp spade and cut out a foot-square strip of lawn about three inches deep. The time for this is after the soil has warmed up and the underground inhabitants have arrived from their hibernating quarters down below the frost line. If he will invert this carefully—he can cut three sides only and hinge it over—and with a small trowel crumble the soil from around the roots, he can poll his grub population

68

for genuine grass roots information. The variety will depend upon where he lives. Some species are national, others prefer the East, South or West, and a few are quite local in their habitat.

His most conspicuous find will likely be a large, fat-looking, white grub. This one will hatch eventually into a big, blundering June bug, also called a May beetle. About two hundred species of these are known in the United States. The grubs may stay in the ground two or three years before graduating into beetles, meanwhile gnawing assiduously for most of the year at the grass roots.

In the eastern states, though not necessarily only there, the next find might likely be a smaller white grub, possibly in numbers. He also feeds on the grass roots, and when he hatches out into a Japanese beetle, will eat almost any kind of flower or foliage. Other possible grub finds may be the young of the Asiatic garden beetle, the oriental beetle, the masked and rose chafers, the green June beetle—a grub that crawls on his back—and the European chafer. This last, new since 1940, is considered to be a bad one, now found mainly in New York state. Authorities are trying hard to keep it from spreading. The C-shaped grubs, about three-quarters of an inch long, are white with brown heads, and are really hard on turf.

If the grub-hunting lawn prospector becomes serious about the business, he will take foot-square surveys in other parts of his domain. If by then he has found an average of more than three grubs to the foot he might do well to inquire for the proper insecticide.

Then, if he is the worrying type, let him be aware that the roots of his grass may also be injured, more or less, by ants, mole crickets, wireworms, wild bees and billbugs. Even earthworms, if they become too numerous, can be nuisances; and in some eastern places he can look for the imported oriental earthworm, much more handsome than our modest native squirmers. Light green above with a purplish-green line down the back, it gets to be six or eight inches long.

While the subterranean workers are chewing away at the roots, another branch of the lawn infantry will be coming forward, ready to forage on the leaves and stems. In this regiment the common soldiers are armyworms, sod webworms, cutworms, billbugs, frit flies, fiery skippers, lucerne moths, leaf bugs, and an occasional grasshopper. In another category are the plant-juice suckers: chinch bugs, false chinch bugs, scale insects, leaf hoppers, meadow spittlebugs, and mites.

The lawn may also harbor a variety of not-so-nice creatures that do no particular damage to the grass. In this group can be ticks, fleas, chiggers, thrips, snails, slugs, millipedes, centipedes, sowbugs, pillbugs, spiders, and, in the South, scorpions. An oddity in this group is a repulsive, reddish-brown insect about three quarters of an inch long that carries a pair of stout forceps on the rear end of its body. This is the European earwig. It emits a vile odor, and likes to feed on kitchen refuse, on zinnias and hollyhocks as well as other flowers, and on garden vegetables; it also likes to hide in a wet mop. So far it appears mostly in the eastern and northwestern states.

Assuming that the suburban outdoorsman has not yet quenched his entomological curiosities and enthusiasms, he need only plant a vegetable garden. On this small tract he will find after the first year from two to three hundred highly interesting insects and plant diseases.

9/Knowledge in the Fruit Trees

ON APRIL 13, 1956, ORLO L. PRIOR OPENED A RIPENED grapefruit he had just picked from one of the trees in the back yard of his Florida home. The interior was filled with unpleasant-looking maggots about three-eighths of an inch long. Realizing that here might be something too dangerous to ignore, he hurried the fruit to the county agricultural agent's office. The worms were identified as larvae of the Mediterranean fruit fly, a foreign pest not seen in Florida since an outbreak had been eradicated twenty-seven years before.

Within a week eleven adult flies had been trapped in nearby areas. The Florida citrus industry knew that it was headed for big trouble.

How the insect had again reached the United States no one could be sure. Perhaps an infested orange, carried in the baggage of an international air traveler and somehow overlooked by the vigilant customs inspectors, had been tossed aside. It could have come from any of the Mediterranean countries, or up from South America.

State and federal fruit fly experts hurried to the Miami area to determine the extent of the infestation and to plan their eradication campaign. Unchecked, the fly could make worthless the vast plantings that glow in the sun across the peninsula's middle. The land itself would fall sharply in value. Much more than the expected millions of citrus income for '56 and '57 was at stake. If the Medfly could not be stopped, the flow of fresh oranges and processed juices to millions of consumers would slow to a trickle and rise to prices that many could not afford. Growers could envisage a housewife slicing into a maggoty fruit and resolving never again to buy a Florida orange or grapefruit. Not only must the fly be controlled; it had to be eradicated.

Long before a victory could be announced, nearly 50,000 traps had been set over the state to discover whether the insect had moved into new areas. The plastic traps, baited with angelica-seed oil until the world supply was exhausted and then with a new, synthetic lure, revealed that the fly had found its way into twenty-eight of Florida's sixty-seven counties.

By April 30, only seventeen days after Orlo Prior opened his wormy grapefruit, ground equipment began pouring out sprays in the first counties. Road blocks were set up to prevent fruit from being carried out. On May 18 airplanes began to take over the spraying job. Fumigation chambers were established so that safe fruit could be freed for shipment. By October 23 a total of 4,672,901 vehicles had been inspected; the road blocks were then no longer considered necessary.

All through the hot summer, through fall and winter, the fight continued. Some seven million acres were covered with baited malathion spray, and more than thirty thousand acres of soil were treated with granular dieldrin to knock out the flies pupating in the ground. Checks by biologists after and during the campaign found that except for a few small fish, no wildlife had been injured.

Nearly eight hundred men had been employed, and $10,000,000 had been spent—half state and half federal funds

—before the time in late 1957 when an announcement could be made that Florida had been freed from the menacing Medfly. Again it could be said that only the United States, of all citrus-producing nations, had totally eradicated the costly pest.

Probably a native of Africa, the Mediterranean fruit fly is troublesome in all the Mediterranean countries and in most other subtropics. Its ravages extend to deciduous fruits as well as to citrus. The peach is one of its preferences; in one year it destroyed four-fifths of Sardinia's peaches. More than 140 different plants are known to be its hosts. The adult is smaller than the housefly, and rather colorful. The female punctures the rind of ripe fruit with a needlelike appendage through which she deposits her eggs. Within two or three days these hatch into cream-colored maggots that, after ruining the fruit, drop to the ground where they remain just beneath the surface in a pupal stage for about ten days. Then they emerge as adults and continue their ruin. One female, who may live as long as a year, will lay as many as eight hundred eggs during her career.

Florida had experienced a previous invasion by the Medfly in 1929, when much less was known about how to down such an enemy. That campaign, when twenty counties were infested, cost $7,500,000, and the labor of nearly five thousand men. Among the measures taken then that better knowledge made unnecessary in 1956 were destruction of some badly infested plantings, the stripping of all fruit from trees, and complete destruction of 625,000 boxes of fruit besides some 50,000 bushels of vegetables. At that time less effective insecticides were available, and airplane spraying had not yet developed to its later efficiency. Again in 1962 the Medfly appeared, but was quickly discovered and reached only three counties. It was fully eradicated within two months. Since 1957, eight thousand traps have been kept in service to give warning of any new invasion.

Early in 1965 the United Nations joined in a project to try

to eliminate the Medfly and to stop its spread in Central America. An outbreak was discovered in Costa Rica in 1955, which spread to Nicaragua and into western Panama. Current damage was being estimated at $7 million a year, with the prospect that the figure would rise to $82 million if the insect were not stopped. A fund of $425,000 authorized by the United Nations was to be supplemented with $824,000 more from the seven Central American countries concerned. For the three-year project it was planned to utilize the method which eradicated the screwworm fly in southeastern United States.

Few of us who view the tempting displays of perfect fruits in today's supermarkets, and who select from them with confidence that every item will be unblemished inside and out, are likely to think of the tremendous efforts expended in the orchards and groves. Fruit that is free from the marks of insect attack comes to market only by dint of constant vigilance, numerous sprays, and careful handling even after harvest.

My father was fond of apples. Before bedtime he loved to bring one or two of his favorites up from the cellar. With his always sharp jackknife he would remove the peel in one unbroken spiral and then enjoy the crisp, cool flesh before winding the old brass clock and retiring. Soon after he acquired his own farm early in the 1890's he set apart an acre and a half and planted it to the varieties he liked best. They ranged from the handsome red-striped Early Harvests and the big yellowish sweet apples that ripened soon after to the juicy fall Wealthies, the Tulpehockens, and others suitable for winter storage. At that time no eastern or midwestern farm was considered well balanced unless it included an apple orchard and plantings of other fruits. Father believed that a farm should be nearly self-sufficient so far as providing food for the household was concerned. He set out plum, cherry, and peach trees, and a variety of berries. All these he had known at his boyhood home where, in a still new country that the insects had not yet invaded, all grew to near perfection. We anticipated the apple pies, apple dumplings, and applesauce, and the fresh and prepared other fruits.

His orchard was a disappointment. By the time it was ready to blossom and bear the insect scourges had arrived. How many of the five hundred different insect species that are reported to attack apples came to our orchard we did not know; but it was rarely that a perfect apple ripened and seldom could more than a bushel or so be picked out that were fit to put into winter storage. The curculio arrived with the plums and peaches, and borers attacked the peach trees until they withered. One by one the trees so hopefully planted were turned to firewood; for as Father studied the problem he saw that it would not pay to divert time from major farm work in order to collect and apply the sprays necessary to protect a few fruits. The old-fashioned farmstead orchard has almost totally disappeared for this reason. The crop and livestock farmer finds it cheaper to buy his fruits and to leave their production to professionals who do not also have acres of field crops to cultivate and herds of livestock to tend.

What, then, does the professional orchardist have to do in order to produce those colorful, shining apples that every supermarket and fruit store displays? The spray schedule prepared by the College of Agriculture at Rutgers for New Jersey apple growers tells some of the story:

In early spring, before the fruit buds show any green, a dormant spray is advised in order to control aphids by killing the overwintering eggs. That's Number One.

As soon as the fruit buds show green tips the time has come for the delayed dormant or green bud spray to control scale, mites, red bug, scab, and mildew. That's Number Two.

Five to ten days later comes the "pre-pink through bloom" spray to control scab. This should be repeated every seven days until the bloom appears. To protect bees, no spray is advised during the period of full bloom. This is Number Three.

After the petals fall and before the calyx closes a spray is scheduled to control codling moth, curculio, red-banded leaf roller, cankerworm, mites, scab and mildew. Number Four.

Seven days after the petals fall comes the "first cover" spraying to defeat the codling moth, curculio, red-banded leaf roller, cankerworm, and scab. Number Five.

Then in seven to ten days the "second cover" spray meets a new threat, fruit spot, in addition to continuing the war on codling moth, curculio, leaf roller, and scab. Number Six.

The man may now be able to take a day off, since the "third cover" spray comes only after a ten or twelve day interval. Then he has twelve days or maybe two weeks before the "fourth cover" treatment. Both of these are aimed to defeat the codling moth, scab, sooty blotch, and fruit spot. Numbers Seven and Eight.

After a similar interval the sprayers take another shot at the four threats just named, along with the red-banded leaf roller and apple maggot. That's Number Nine.

Besides these nine standard spray treatments, after the middle of July a second brood of codling moths may appear and call for a special spray. White rot, black rot, and fire blight offer additional hazards in some orchards.

The New Jersey apple man does not storm into his orchard with one simple mixture for all problems. He may have to deal with two or three dozen different ingredients in exact and precise quantities and proportions. He is sharply warned that certain of them are "extremely poisonous to human beings and other warm-blooded animals" and admonished that he had better take all the precautions printed on the package or prescribed by the manufacturer, or else not use the materials at all. He must take care that the used containers are so disposed of as to do no harm. Boldface type emphasizes the specific number of days that must elapse after the final applications before harvest is begun; this, of course, is to make sure that no hurtful residues will remain on the fruit.

Another complication for the orchardist arises from the fact that different varieties of apples may respond differently to the same spray, so he has to fit his mixtures to the variety. Nor are the insects and mites the sprays destroy his only concern. In cold weather, mice like to tunnel under the grass and snow cover to the trees to gnaw at the bark, and if numerous may seriously damage or kill the trees. Since he can't spray the mice, the only preventive is to place lethal baits in tunnels and trails where the rodents may find them before they reach the trees. Still further, the orchard man has pruning and fertilizing to do.

All these procedures are expensive. The pesticides are not cheap and labor is costly. They are used for the simple reason that if they were not, as Dr. Byron Shaw, administrator of the USDA Agricultural Research Service, explained in a very few words:

"We wouldn't have any apple crop on the market, as we know that crop today."

Speaking of peaches, Dr. Shaw has said that ". . . certainly in the eastern United States it would be almost impossible to grow marketable peaches without sprays."

The peach orchardist's schedule is fully as exacting as that of the apple grower, and his hazards add up to an even longer list. Conditions from which in New Jersey he must protect his crops include: leaf curl, scale, brown rot, peach canker, mildews, curculio, mites, oriental fruit moth, bacterial spot, tarnished plant bug, green soldier bug, peach tree borer, two-spotted mites, and European red mites.

Pears, plums, cherries, and grapes all demand protection from insect and disease pests if they are to mature into acceptable fruit. Profitable crops of blueberries, raspberries, blackberries, and strawberries can be brought to market only by growers who know the enemies and deal with them at the appropriate times with the right chemical ammunition. Occasional backyard patches may yield an output satisfactory to a home owner without the rigorous attention the commercial grower must pay; even so, the householder may find his efforts defeated by pests that in his optimism he did not anticipate nor prevent.

Millions of us who like strawberries agree with the oft-quoted words uttered some four hundred years ago by Dr. William Butler, who remarked, "Doubtless God could have made a better berry, but doubtless God never did." The farmers who raise them have tried for decades, though, to make strawberries better, and have been able to set their rows with many flavorful, improved varieties. Insects and insect-spread diseases work equally hard to keep the strawberry crop down.

The grower these days is advised to plant his new setting as far as he can from other strawberries, in land that has not grown any for three years. His new field should have been in a clean-cultivated crop the year before, and by no means where corn, weeds or grass have been plowed under.

The reasons for such precautions are the more than two dozen kinds of aphids, mites, weevils and other pests that attack the plants or share man's fondness for the berries. The aphids spread virus diseases that inhibit the plant's growth and productivity. The cyclamen mite, so small that one must use a magnifying glass to see him at all, stunts the plants and in a season can make a strawberry bed useless. Lygus bugs cause the berries to become woody in texture. Ants cause damage by their efforts to encourage and care for the aphids who are their milk cows; the ants live on honeydew excreted by their aphids. Thrips, snails, borers, wireworms, and others keep the plants from thriving or damage the fruit.

The box of red, ripe strawberries one brings from the roadside stand or market counter these days represents a farmers' and scientists' triumph. After all his precautions and careful cultivation, the grower usually has to resort to a few dusts or sprays to rescue his crop from the bugs and diseases—bugs and diseases that neither old Dr. Butler, nor Ike Walton who made his saying famous by quoting it in *The Compleat Angler,* had reason to know about in their times.

California farmers provide their fellow Americans with a greater volume of fruits, and more kinds of them, than are grown in any other state. They ship fresh, canned, frozen, and dried, in abundance and quality, to all corners of the country, with some left over for export. To maintain their far-flung markets they must produce fruits that are clean, unblemished, and in every respect safe.

A faint idea of the struggle to grow acceptable fruits may be obtained if one leafs through the sixty-four-page mimeographed book that instructs citrus growers in how to control the pests that infest their groves. Seven entomologists from the University of California's Citrus Research Center and Agricultural Experiment Station at Riverside join to prepare the book, which is revised each year. The ten most troublesome enemies of citrus include five species of scale insects, three kinds of mites, a thrip, and a leaf roller. The book lists eighteen others that also may need attention. The growers are told in detail how much pesticide to apply, when to do it, what varieties to treat and by what method. A table sets out the facts about compatibility of each pesticide with others. They are warned specifically about what may endanger wildlife and bees, or cause other hazards. "THE GROWER IS RESPONSIBLE," a capitalized statement says, "for residues on his crops as well as for problems caused by drift from his property to other properties or crops."

Growers of California pears had in hand for 1965 a twelve-page printed booklet with equally detailed instructions for treatment at twelve successive intervals. The more serious pear pests are pear psylla, mealy bug, codling moth, and European red mite; several others are listed. Similar manuals are prepared for growers of apples, prunes, grapes, peaches, melons, and for the vegetable and field crop farmers. Fruit producers in all the states obtain instructions from their own experiment stations. We have cited those from New Jersey and California; the problems are different elsewhere only in minor details due to weather and soils.

Despite every endeavor to cope with the bugs, success is so far incomplete. Yields do get reduced. Volumes of damaged fruits do not qualify for the markets Californians struggled so long to build against the obstacles of distance, irrigation costs, and other handicaps not shared by eastern competitors.

The California State Department of Agriculture undertakes annually to estimate the losses due to pests and to the necessities for control expenditures. For 1963 these estimates, compiled from county reports, showed that farmers after spending $80 million to apply pesticides still suffered measurable yield losses on all crops of nearly $150 million. Animal pests added another burden of $3 million. Losses of nearly $17 million in forest stumpage, mostly from ten different insects, also were recorded.

The report indicates that of California's 36 million acres in farms about 8½ million acres underwent pest control treatments. Airplanes spread more than 80 per cent of the sprays and dusts. The state lists 509 airplane pilots and 250 apprentice pilots engaged in such work, and 1,482 licensed pest control professionals.

Neither these California growers, nor their fellow producers elsewhere of our most varied and finest fruits will argue with the lines of Sir John Denham:

> The tree of knowledge blasted by dispute
> Produces sapless leaves instead of fruit.

10/Peas at a Penny Each

SELDOM CAN A GREAT CHANGE IN THE AMERICAN STAND-
ards and ways of living be attributed to one single factor. Nor
do great changes often appear and become suddenly accepted
by nearly everyone. Perhaps television and penicillin can be
cited as approximate exceptions.

Only those who have been around for five or six decades
are likely to remember clearly that not so long ago for most
people fresh vegetables in winter were simply not to be
found or were highly expensive. Most of any winter's vegetable diet came from cans. The quick-freezing process did not
become really commercial until in the early 1930's and required years for improvement and consumer acceptance. Of
the leafy vegetables, an occasional cabbage represented the
supply, and in many parts of the country no stores could offer
even that.

Now the shopping housewife pushes her supermarket cart
with hardly a thought of the growing seasons. She finds lettuce and romaine, endive, brussel sprouts, broccoli and spinach available for Christmas and Groundhog Day as readily as
for the Fourth of July. If she craves ripe tomatoes, egg plant
or fresh cucumbers, they await her hand. Since 1930 our con-

sumptions of health-building fruits and vegetables has nearly doubled.

Transportation, refrigeration and demand for quality all have had parts in this change, which is indeed a very great one. The innovation that has contributed by far the most, however, has been the chemical industry's development and production of materials that make economical and quality production possible.

The flow of winter vegetables into the northern cities begins from around the nation's southern perimeter. In southern Florida, along the lower Rio Grande in Texas, in southern Arizona and California, sunshine keeps soil and air warm enough for plants to grow. The farmer who ventures into the off-season vegetable business, nevertheless, takes his risks with each crop. Icy northern temperatures may invade his domain for just long enough to freeze a whole crop into trash, after all the investment in work, fertilizers, sprays, and cultivations. Fortunately that disaster does not strike every year or every crop. Always, however, the plagues of insects, weeds, and plant diseases threaten. Not just one species, but any one of several may build up to destructive numbers.

Each crop attracts its own special bugs, and each area contains a few that particularize as to their geography. The summer grower up north has to fight just as does his winter friend on the sunny southern borders, though not quite so hard. Whether he raises sweet corn in Maine, onions in New York, peas in Minnesota or beans in Washington, the baneful pests will be there with him, too.

The chain of authority which the vegetable farmer must obey is ruthless. The housewife who finds aphids in her spinach or a worm in her cabbage explodes promptly and indignantly to the store manager. He passes the problem on to chain-store executives who know which warehousers and wholesalers handled the offending produce, and it bounds on back to the original buyers and to the farmers. The grower is left with no doubt that if he expects to keep his market he had better keep his aphids and worms and all their traces out of every vegetable he sells.

More than this, the farmer knows that whatever he plants, from asparagus to zucchini, he will have only as much crop to sell as the insects will permit him to grow. They show no concern for the housewife's sensitivity nor for the farmer's hopes. His troubles start early. Indeed, in the autumn before seeding time he may need to fumigate the soil itself to blast tiny nematodes that assail plant roots. He may have to treat the seeds themselves before planting to avoid some canker or wilt. Cutworms will gnaw off the stems and kill the plant overnight before it has put much more than a tentative green sprout into the air. From then on the sap suckers, leaf chewers and companion hordes will contest for the crop, destroying plants, stunting growth, spreading disease organisms, unless he defeats their intentions first.

If the housewife is to have her clean vegetables and if the farmer is to make his crop he has to use the weapons that work best. That is no simple matter, either. The south Jersey grower, for instance, is presented by his experiment station with recommendations that include three dozen kinds of insecticides, from which he must choose the ones considered best for his particular problems at each particular point in the growing period. If he is a specialist, growing only one or a few kinds of crops, of course he does not have to use three dozen insecticides, but he may have to apply a half-dozen or more to meet conditions as they develop during the season.

The chemists who create the insecticides unquestionably are learned men in their fields who do a marvelous job. They scan and test thousands of compounds to isolate the specific one that is selective enough to decimate a particular class of insects without producing other unwanted effects. The farmer, too, has to become something of a chemist to make his decisions, and then he must follow the directions completely to the last letter and period or endanger his success.

The bugs, however, may be even better chemists in their

ways than are the chemists themselves. One of the unsolved entomological mysteries is why and how the insects can be so selective. Some are omnivorous or, as the entomologist would say, polyphagous; that is, they will eat from a wide variety of plants. The boll weevil is rated as monophagous, having been seen to eat from no other vegetation except the cotton plant. In between are the oliphagous insects which confine their diets to a small range of similar plants, or even to one family of plants. The Colorado potato beetle seldom bothers any except the Solanaceous family, the potato and its nightshade relatives, including the tomato and egg plant.

Another phase of insect chemistry seems to be better understood by the bugs than by human chemists. They are scientific at choosing their baby foods. The common monarch butterfly, for example, flits from flower to flower sipping the nectar. But when time comes for the serious business of raising a family, the monarch goes only to the milkweed. There, when the eggs hatch, the young will find the only food that makes them thrive. Similarly, the cabbage butterfly in its adult, winged stage alights in all sorts of places, but heads for the cabbage plant to place the eggs—there, its offspring will find their only acceptable food.

Possibly each family of plants disperses a distinctive odor that attracts its own particular insect boarders; or perhaps within its complex construction some chemical or compound, as yet undiscovered by seeking man, supplies the specific nourishment that the insect requires. The bug experts have long known, or at least suspected, that insects possess a sense of smell far keener, far more sensitive than the human or even canine olfactory equipment. Extracts from the female scent factors in certain species have attracted male response from long distances: if man once fully learns to extract or synthesize these lures, as he has done with a few, he will conquer more of his so far elusive enemies.

Those enemies number in the hundreds—far too many to

even begin to list here. They are serious pests that, if un-checked and uncontrolled, would not only make impossible our all-year abundance and variety of clean and nearly per-fect vegetable foods but at many times would denude the counters of those we now find there.

Most commercial growers of vegetables must follow spray schedules as exacting and usually as numerous as those for fruit growers. The numbers of pests are no fewer. If the vegetable grower has any advantage over the fruit grower it is only that since most of his plants are annuals, each year he has a chance to start afresh.

The housewife, incidentally, is not the only exacting and persnickety customer of the vegetable farmer. The food pro-cessor, the canner, freezer, soup maker, pickle maker, and the baby-food manufacturer are all big buyers of vegetables. Usu-ally they contract with farmer producers in advance of each season. They can be even more particular than the housewife because they have better, more direct facilities for enforcing their demands. No soup manufacturer wants to learn that any consumer—she is his boss, too—has found a faulty bit of vegetable in one of his cans. No canner or freezer ever wants to face the likelihood of a customer's discovering traces of bug damage on his peas or broccoli. Companies that contract for large quantities of vegetables will go so far as to visit the proposed growing fields in advance of planting and to test soil samples to make certain that no undue pesticidal residues remain from previous years that could possibly appear in the forthcoming crop, especially if it is to be a root crop. And they are equally vigilant that none of the harvested crops bring undesirable materials to their processing plants.

The notorious ability of so many insects to produce num-erous generations in one season enables them to infest their available food supply, however large it may be. When a farmer plants a twenty-acre field to peas or cabbage he un-avoidably issues an irresistible invitation to the banqueting bugs. The more there is to eat, the more insects will appear to eat it. If the grower is to keep the supply rolling toward the market counters, and if he is to stay in business, he has no choice except to apply measures that will keep the enemies under control.

If he had to pick off the destroyers by hand—and some few eyes can see—peas at a penny apiece would be cheap and might cost a nickel.

11/No Crop Is Exempt

CHEWING AND BITING; CRUNCHING AND SUCKING; PUNCTUR-
ing and cutting; tunneling and boring; flying and buzzing;
crawling and creeping; squirming and wiggling; dirtying and
defiling; stinging and blistering; sapping and debilitating;
corrupting and crippling; fouling and infecting; wounding
and killing; tainting and contaminating; webbing and stunting; forever breeding, hatching, reproducing, multiplying;
underground, above ground and in the air; attacking roots,
stems, leaves, bark, wood, blossoms, grain and fruit; hiding,
often unseen or invisible.

Insects! No farm is free from them. No acre, no square
foot. No crop is exempt; no grain, no grass, no vegetable, no
tree, no animal.

All of us are addicted to bread and butter, meat, milk, and
eggs, the basic foods that stoke our human fires. Not until the
great staple crops are grown do these reach our tables. The
good red meats, the dairy items, poultry, and eggs come only
after the creatures from which they derive have been gener-
ously fed. The animals manufacture our health-giving foods

from the nutrients that the crops of grain, grasses, and legumes (and cotton, too) supply for them.

We might not all walk in hunger if only fruits and vegetables reached our tables; but even if those could come in sufficient quantities we soon would clamor for the big staples that satisfy the inner man. On millions of acres, farmers devote their years to growing these major and most essential crops.

The simplest dictionary definition describes farming as "the act or business of cultivating land." So stated, farming sounds as though it might be a very undemanding bucolic activity, little more than plowing, planting, and harvesting. Actually, of course, as a more complete definition would spell out and as all farmers well know, the annual contest with insects and weeds may be a bigger part of farming than the plowing and reaping.

Because some of the insects are so small, secretive, and insidious, farmers may not always realize why their crop yields disappoint their hopes. Their awareness becomes acute, however, when the boll weevil visibly devastates the cotton, the European corn borers break over the corn tassels, or the aphids thin the alfalfa to the verge of failure.

Except for mosquitoes, the cotton boll weevil has precipitated more investigation, cost farmers more money, received more curses and prompted more constructive actions than any insect. After being fought for more than half a century it still takes a toll of $300 million or more from cotton growers each year. Of all farm-used insecticides, a third or more are poured out to check the boll weevil. The applications, made six to a dozen times or even more a season, cost $10 to $20 an acre each crop year, and with bad infestations may cost twice that.

This spectacularly successful, long-nosed little creature crossed the Rio Grande into Texas about 1892. A few years elapsed before he found enough cotton to spread himself, but early in the twentieth century he began business in a big way. Communities were ravaged; stores closed, and in two counties nearly two-thirds of the farmers gave up. Could the weevil be stopped?

"Impossible," one farmer was reported as saying. "I bottled them up in pure alcohol and they only got staggering drunk. I sealed them in a tin can, threw the can into a brush heap and set it afire. When the solder melted the red-hot weevils flew out and set my barn afire."

Possibly that story bears a touch of Texas overstatement. The man may not have had a barn.

Nevertheless the weevil steadily ate his way, forty to 160 miles a year, until from Texas to Virginia he topped every list of the ten least wanted insects. He completely extinguished the old and famous sea island cotton industry along the southeastern coast.

The weevil hibernates over winter in vegetation and trash near the cotton fields, and emerges in spring. The female punctures and lays eggs in the squares or in the bolls. Infested squares and bolls will drop off, or the fiber within will fail to mature properly, will be stained and the useful seed will be damaged.

If the weevil were human, we should be obliged to admire him. The obstacles in his life are abundant. He may die between the time he rises from hibernation and cotton grows enough to start his season. Heat and dry weather prevent his young from living. Birds eat the adults. Some native predatory and parasitic insects slay him. Introduced parasites are aimed at him. Farming practices are changed to cause him trouble and inconvenience. Farmers have hurled insecticides of several kinds and combinations of kinds at him from ground and air.

Yet, for 1950, the boll weevil achieved his peak up to that time, with damage figured by the National Cotton Council at $907,884,000—nearly a billion. During five of the preceding forty years the loss had been estimated at more than half a billion; in every year it had been substantial.

Since we do not eat cotton, and have several alternative

choices among fibers, does that matter much to those of us
not directly concerned with cotton? Well, let's pursue National Cotton Council figures a little further. Take 1946,
when old boll weevil and his companions in the bug business
knocked off more than 15 per cent of the cotton crop and lost
the nation 613,000 tons of cotton seed, about $44 million
worth. The oil from that much seed could have made more
than a third of the margarine eaten that year; it could have
taken care of eight million peoples' total minimum edible
fat requirements. After the oil was removed, the high protein
meal remaining could have been fed to cattle to produce 178
million more pounds of beef than we had, or nineteen additional quarts of milk for every individual then in the U.S.A.

Two credits belong to the boll weevil, one an expansion in
aviation and the other a new concept in education.

The airplane first became an agricultural implement in
the 1920's when cotton growers found that it was economical
for applying dusts and sprays against the boll weevil at the
right times, regardless of ground conditions. Since then agricultural flying has become a considerable business. Rice often
is sown from the air, as are grass seeds, especially in rough
range terrain. In the late 1940's sprays were added to the
aerial repertoire.

The agricultural extension system, with its county agents,
home demonstration agents, 4-H Club agents and many specialists has been called the greatest adult educational force
ever created. The system developed from early efforts by Dr.
Seaman A. Knapp to show farmers that by rotating their
crops and adopting better farm practices they could contend
with the weevil. His idea that "what a man does himself he
cannot doubt" was the basis of the extension idea. Without
doubt the weevil did compel farmers to venture into other
profitable crops as well as to adopt better methods with
cotton. In Coffee County, Alabama, recognition of this took
the form of a monument, erected to the boll weevil in the
public square of Enterprise, the county seat.

So we give the devil his due.

The cotton grower, unfortunately, does not depend solely upon the boll weevil to wreck his year. He must also contend with cotton aphids, spider mites, cotton leaf worm, tarnished and rapid plant bugs, thrips, tobacco budworm, grasshoppers, bollworm, cotton flea hopper, fall army worm, garden webworm and southern green stink bug, to name a few of the evils, generally lesser though not always trifling.

The boll weevil specializes in cotton. His rival, the bollworm, will work on almost anything, especially if it is valuable. Known also as the corn-ear worm and tomato fruitworm, this insect does its worst in the mid-south, Mississippi to Texas, but operates in many other places.

Then there is the constant threat by that international cotton bandit, the pink bollworm, already established in most leading cotton-producing countries and since 1917 a target of desperate efforts to keep him from obtaining naturalization here. No insects destroy so much of China's cotton; Brazil loses from 20 per cent to more than 50 per cent of the crop each year. The Plant Pest Control and Plant Quarantine division of USDA maintains an unceasing vigil. Any spot known to become infested by pink bollworm is immediately quarantined. State regulations, some fairly severe, are invoked. A cooperative agreement with Mexico provides help on both sides of the Rio Grande. Years of toilsome effort have been directed toward extinction of wild cotton, a host plant in southern Florida and always a potential source of infestations northward. Insecticidal and cultural controls have so far kept the pink bollworm from matching the boll weevil's devastation. The fight costs money—but an uncontrolled pink bollworm would cost vastly more.

The European corn borer is not much less economical to maintain than the boll weevil. For eleven years, 1950–61, in field corn alone the losses averaged 107 million bushels a year, worth somewhere near $200 million to farmers and a great deal more to the national economy. Sweet-corn losses were additional, plus whatever it did to sorghums, soybeans, potatoes, oats and others, along with several of the common and popular garden flowers. It infests more than two hundred species of plants.

Beginning an American career in 1917 in Massachusetts, the borer promptly set out to see the country. In the late twenties quarantines and road blocks were maintained in hope that the great corn belt beginning in western Ohio might not be invaded. The borer evaded the quarantine and struck across the corn lands to as far west as the Rockies. Entomologists rushed to Europe and Asia to hunt for natural enemies; of twenty-one introduced, only four have done much to reduce the borer numbers. A few native insects, lady beetles and lacewings notably, occasionally eat the eggs. Woodpeckers and blackbirds devour the larvae, which appear in two broods each season. Insecticides have afforded reliable control of the borer in sweet corn, but the insect maintains reserves in many plants other than corn, which the sprays do not reach. Resistant corn hybrids that are much less seriously injured have been developed by plant breeders and entomologists. In 1949, its peak year so far, corn-borer damage in twenty-nine states reached nearly $350 million.

The adult insect is a moth. The larva, which wreaks the havoc, will bore into almost any part of the plant from roots to tassels and ears, but most often will be found in the stalks. The plant's vigor declines; the injuries invite bacteria and other causes of disease. Stalks break easily, and at worst no usable grain matures.

A detailed account of the attrition that insects impose upon crops could be monotonous; we shall try only to indicate its variety and extent. From the moment a farmer plants a seed after he has plowed and fitted his ground, bugs numerous in kind and myriad in numbers begin their campaigns. Seldom do they fail to prevent his yield from reaching its full potential. Yet to the casual observer, their depredations may be hardly apparent.

The bits of foamy froth one sees occasionally on legumes or weeds in spring would seem to be quite innocuous. Young nymphs of the meadow spittle bug suck sap from the plant, excrete a fluid, and pump air through it in such a way as to build these damp shelters for themselves. A heavy infestation can cut a hay crop by a fourth, or even by a half.

Another sap-sucking insect, the spotted alfalfa aphid, has lowered the alfalfa crop's value by more than $40 million a year. A newcomer, first noted in 1954, it needed only five years to reach thirty-three states. The potato leafhopper, pea aphid, alfalfa weevil and alfalfa caterpillar enlarge the losses. In some areas, if there were no insecticides, this highly essential forage could not be grown profitably.

More than one hundred pests assail the potato plant, eating the stems and leaves, damaging the tubers and carrying virus diseases. It was a virus, probably aided by insects, that caused the pitiful Irish potato famine in the late 1840's. The new insecticides have in several areas improved potato yields by 60 per cent.

Grasshopper raids year after year destroy crops and pastures at an annual rate usually exceeding $20 million; in 1936 the estimated damage ran above $100 million. Chinch bugs, Hessian flies and green bugs among others rival the grasshoppers' annual destructiveness.

Geneticists and entomologists cooperate to develop crop varieties able to resist insect assaults. Predators and parasites are introduced and encouraged. Farmers try to change their planting, fertilizing and other plans to avoid or avert the pest attacks. But the chewing and sucking and boring continue. It would be interesting, and probably appalling, if a competent and conservative economic entomologist were to undertake to estimate the inevitable crop disasters that would befall if nothing could be done to stop the bugs.

Even the insecticides do a less than perfect job. Somewhere in the future, with vastly greater knowledge of insect and plant biology than now exists, science may break through with completely new miracle weapons, some hydrogen bomb for insect warfare. With 7,000 or more new people calling every day for their bread, butter and meat, a period will come when the margin of insect losses will be found too great to tolerate. Then, indeed, "bugs or people" will be a burning question. Meanwhile, it is fortunate that the presently known weapons work as well as they do at holding in check the voracious insect hordes.

The plants, of course, can indicate their troubles only as men learn to recognize the bugs and symptoms. Animals can do better, even though imperfectly, at telling man about their ailments.

12 / Freedom from Dumb Misery

YOU MIGHT NOT LIKE TO BE A HORSE OR A COW. THE disadvantages are extensive, particularly when hurt, sick, or annoyed.

An animal's tail performs poorly as an insecticide. The fly it disturbs will move for an instant, only to return to the same or to a more vulnerable spot. A horse's hooves and tail provide little protection against winged and crawling annoyances. Anyone will be sympathetic who has watched a horse in harness, or even one free in a pasture, trying in a desperate frenzy to fight off the botflies that are determined to lay eggs on his lower forelegs or in his nasal passages.

As a sentient being, any animal is fully capable of conscious feeling. Hear the anguished squeals of a captured rabbit or the yelp of a stoned dog! When it suffers disease, or injury from insect bites, its misery is real. One has only to look at a fevered, drooping creature to know that its response to sickness includes bodily suffering probably no different from that which humans experience. Its remedies are fewer, and may be nonexistent unless man intervenes.

Every animal everywhere, apparently not even excepting the whales at sea, has its quota of tiny enemies. Some are

95

annoying, some painful, some can and do kill. In addition to
the hosts of insects proper, animals are constantly attacked by
other arthropods, the great numbers of fleas, ticks, mites, and
lice.

Viewed only from an economic angle, without thought of
the discomfort, a miserable animal may die, or be stunted in
growth, a dairy cow may give less milk, and they will bring
less profit when sold. United States farmers will have on hand
at one time more than 100 million cattle, 60 million hogs, 30
million sheep, 4 million goats, 375 million chickens and 7
million turkeys. An estimate by USDA authorities nearly fifteen years ago set the annual livestock losses from insects and
related pests at half a billion dollars and pronounced their
guess then to be a conservative one. With higher prices and
greater numbers of animals, the figure by now might well
approach or exceed a billion dollars.

It may justly be said that many millions of people owe
their lives today to the conquest of one prevalent animal pest.
Back in the seventies and eighties of the nineteenth century,
Texas fever caused enormous losses among cattle. Southern
cattle suffered from the fever, and if they were moved to
northern ranges whole new herds caught it and died. These
losses became so formidable that Congress appropriated
money to discover what could be done.

After a patient research effort nearly a decade long, Dr.
Theobald Smith determined that a tick transmitted the fever,
and that if the ticks could be destroyed the fever losses
would end. Smith's findings produced proof, the first in medical history, that an insect could carry a disease organism
from one body to another. Others, pursuing this fundamental
new fact, were able to identify the vectors of yellow fever,
malaria and various human plagues.

A massive battle against the Texas fever tick continued for
half a century. Federal and state livestock officials carried on
a continuous educational campaign among cattle owners, and

then supervised actual operations as millions of cattle were run, at repeated intervals, through dipping vats. Only in the recent past could it be said that the fever had been wiped out from the United States, and the tick itself virtually exterminated from the country. The few localized outbreaks of ticks that have since occurred have been quickly controlled. Vigilance continues, because in Latin America and the tropics ticks and fever continue their deadly havoc.

Not fatal, but expensive, the cattle grub has been fought for years by livestock men and scientists, aided by much organized effort. This is probably our country's most costly cattle pest. Annual losses are estimated at from $200 to $400 million.

The adult of the grub begins its ravages as the heel fly. At this stage the small pest darts at the animal to lay eggs, preferably on the hairs around the heel. Cattle apparently know something of the consequences if the flies succeed. Although the egg laying causes them no pain, the animals run about in frenzied fashion, their tails in the air; in stampede, if the herd is large, some may injure others simply by reckless running. If they can find water to stand in, or deep shade, they will take refuge there for hours and refuse to pursue their normal grazing.

When the eggs are hatched the young larva penetrates the skin and lives for a few weeks on the tissues within. There are two species. One kind moves along until it gets to the viscera or esophagus, and the other works its way along the spinal canal. After some months the young grub bores an air hole through the skin along the animal's back and encloses itself within a sort of cyst at that point until in about three months it matures. Small lumps on the host's back indicate their presence at this period. After all these interesting interior adventures they emerge and drop to the ground, where they stay under some protective object for another period until they become flies.

During their eight to eleven months' tour of the inner animal, the grubs affect growth and meat production adversely. After slaughter the butcher has to remove all the tissue near the cysts, or warbles as they are commonly called, and downgrades the carcass. This adds several dollars to the loss already caused by the animal's inability to do well. Further, a hide punctured by from one to five dozen holes loses most of its value for leather.

Until a decade ago no easy way to combat the cattle grub was found, despite years of research and trial. A few insecticides could be applied to the animals as sprays or dusts with some effect. Cooperative efforts by all cattle owners on a township or larger scale could reduce heel fly numbers substantially if all the cattle in the area were treated three or four times a year for three years or more. This was worthwhile but laborious and expensive. Then it was found that by drenching cattle (that means dosing them internally through the mouth, not soaking them!) with a new systemic insecticide all stages of the grub could be killed. No residue was left in the meat. Further work brought about ways to apply systemics by spraying, dipping, or pouring on along the back, that were equally effective and much easier than compelling a large animal to drink from a bottle. One systemic can be given in feed or salt. No residue appears in milk if the treatment precedes the cow's freshening for a prescribed period.

During warm weather, cattle are pestered by a half-size fly that may have no brains but knows enough to gather in large numbers on the back where the victim can reach neither with switching tail nor swinging head. To avoid rain or too hot sun the flies merely move to the animal's underside. This species is called the horn fly because in cool hours it moves to the base of the horns. These biting, bloodsucking flies are so annoying that they can cause a healthy bovine to worry off a half pound of weight in a day's time. When fresh droppings appear behind the animal the female flies leave off biting long enough to plant a supply of eggs from which, in a fortnight, more flies arise.

When the cattle owner sets up two posts fifteen or twenty feet apart, suspends a chain loosely between them, and wraps the chain with burlap soaked in an insecticidal oil solution, the cattle themselves will treat the horn flies by rubbing their backs under the chain.

Stable flies, deer flies, and the big green-eyed horseflies all bite and suck blood, impose annoyance and discomfort on their victims, and may at times transmit disease to humans.

The botfly, a nasty rascal among flies, feared by animals and in some species dangerous to people, nevertheless boasts some distinctions. For one, no insect is known to exceed his speed of forty to fifty miles an hour. For another, one of his kind catches mosquitoes but does not eat them. This one is called the human botfly. Apparently aware that people and animals will oppose her intentions, the female goes to a nearby marshy area where mosquitoes are numerous, grabs one, and after a moment releases it. In the brief meanwhile she fastens a few of her eggs on the mosquito's underside. She turns it loose, expecting that sooner or later it, or another bearing her eggs, will alight on the skin of a human being or of some warm-blooded animal. While the mosquito probes for blood the eggs are warmed by the skin; hatch immediately; and the larvae bore into the body.

An African species of botfly normally annoys the hippopotamus, but if it can manage it will insert its eggs into human nasal passages. The larvae, when they hatch, will make their way into the sinuses or into the eyes. Blindness results if they are not promptly removed.

The sheep botfly, too, will dart to the eye of a human being, deposit a minute drop from which spiny larvae emerge to crawl over and inflame the eyeball. Attacks upon herders in North Africa have been reported to cause blindness.

A long, tedious list of insects, ticks, lice, and mites bother wild animals and domestic livestock in various ways. Numbers of them only bite and feed on blood. Others make their way under the skin and torment a helpless beast by the itching they cause. Many convey internal parasites, which infest internal organs and sap the animal's vigor and vitality.

Even though their lives are controlled and terminated, domestic animals nowadays generally enjoy a freedom from misery that their wild fellows probably seldom approach. Game experts will testify to the prevalence of pests, discomforts, and diseases among the creatures they study. The modern livestock farmer knows that he simply cannot afford to let his animals remain unhealthy. He also knows what to do for them, or how to find out quickly from his county agent or veterinarian when his practiced eye detects suspicious symptoms.

It is not only the contented cow that gives the most and best milk. The cheerful steer makes the best beef and the happy hen lays the most eggs. No one can prove this better than the keen, present-day farmers.

Hogs, for instance, are readily susceptible to troubles. In the old times, when they were wrongly regarded as naturally filthy animals, they had plenty of troubles. From the debris and dirt of ill-kept quarters they picked up parasites, and if permitted to roam and root in the fields and woods they collected others from the grubs and worms they gathered from underground. The up-to-date hog lives far differently. His boss has become a crank on sanitation. He is born under conditions as nearly sterile as they can be made, and grows up in clean surroundings. If permitted at all to spend time in a pasture, nose rings will discourage his impulse to root, and the field will have been rotated from previous uses so that little chance remains that he may pick up an infection. His sleeping quarters are hosed out frequently. His diet provides minerals and medicaments that fill him with vitality and health.

The poultryman who shelters thousands of birds under one roof can be ruined by any kind of bug that spreads disease through his flock. He, too, practices sanitation and unflagging vigilance. The dairyman has to keep clean and healthy cows if he is to be allowed by authorities to sell his milk. Cattle and sheep ranchers and feeders watchfully guard the well-being of their charges.

In land, buildings, machines, and in animals, every livestock farmer has a heavy investment, running into high thousands that would make many a "small businessman" feel smaller. When the animals provide his main or only source of income, he wisely protects them against illnesses and against the pests that reduce their usefulness or produce the ailments.

Modern science has developed means such as never before existed to protect livestock from pests and diseases. Practically no insect, tick, louse, or mite infesting animals can now be said to be beyond control by some combination of ingredients in sprays, dusts, or dips, or in feeds.

True, not all of them are yet controlled; otherwise the multimillion dollar losses would not continue. But without the controls now known the losses would jump from the conservative seven-figure estimates into ten-figure disasters. Meats, dairy, and poultry products would be less safe to eat and much more expensive. We Americans who can afford our ample supplies of proteins, as most of us do, may well be grateful that pesticides help to make them abundant and so well within our reach.

The unpestered animals may not realize what has been done for them; but they do live in a state of health and comfort that would have greatly eased the lives of their ancestors only a few generations back.

13/The Harvest Is In

THE HARVEST IS IN! THE PLOWING, FERTILIZING, CULTI-vating, spraying, weeding, all have been done. The combines and pickers have been put away. The trucks have delivered to barn, granary, and elevator the grains of the year. The money and the labor have been spent. From here on, everything's hunky-dory. "Comfortably nice," that means, saith Webster.

Ah, but no! declareth Jeremiah (8:20): "The harvest is past, the summer is ended, and we are not saved."

Not saved indeed, not if the granary weevil, the black weevil, the Angoumois grain moth, and the lesser grain borer have their ways, along with that delightfully named but otherwise objectionable "confused flour beetle." Our research so far has failed to reveal why this one is confused, nor why his close cousin, the "depressed flour beetle," is depressed.

Not saved for sure if the khapra beetle ever gets loose in this great grain-producing nation. That one is a menace!

In the marvelous adaptability of nature, nothing comes more naturally than that a category of insects should have been created to wait around until man accumulates the fruits of his harvest and puts them away in what he hopes may be a safe place. There the bug finds a store of plenty. Unlike his outdoor relatives, he has no fear that drouth, flood, or hail may curtail his opportunity to prosper at man's expense. Now is his opportunity to dig in on man's hopes to make a few dollars by holding good foods until they are needed or can be processed. Here in the storage rooms, concentrated plenty awaits.

More than fifty pests assail grains—wheat, rice, barley, oats, rye, corn, sorghums—while they are in storage; and vast quantities always are being held somewhere on farms, in country elevators, huge terminal elevators or processing plants, awaiting their hour of usefulness. The four pests named above are the most common storage insects now in this country. Bins and elevators, boxcars and truck bodies, ships and sacks provide them waiting places and transportation. As a rule they are tiny creatures, an eighth of an inch long or less. They can hide in cracks, live in dust piles, crawl behind car linings and into sack folds. Some species begin their lives in the grain fields and follow the harvest to storage. Others inhabit flour mills. Only alert watchfulness and vigorous efforts at disinfecting all the hiding places can keep them down. Stored grain losses up to $240 million a year have been reported, even after several years of campaigns to reduce and prevent them.

One much-feared pest has—so far—barely obtained a claw-hold in the United States. The khapra beetle has spread from its native southeast Asia to England, Europe, Africa, Japan, the Philippines, and Australia. Isolated infestations have been spotted in California, Arizona, Texas, and Mexico. These have been vigorously handled by federal and state agencies. A heavily infested storage is totally enclosed in polyethylene tarpaulin. Deadly gases are pumped in and held at least forty-eight hours. The adjoining grounds are thoroughly treated three times with a malathion solution, raked

and harrowed to assure complete application. In smaller infestations the treatment is less severe, but the premises are
inspected regularly for a year before being released from
regulation.

Quarantine officers at every seaport and international airport keep on the alert for the khapra beetle. Now that foreign shipping can move up the St. Lawrence Seaway to Chi-
cago and Duluth, the boats arriving at lake ports, too, are
thoroughly searched. Were the khapra ever to find itself free
in the great grain-storage cities of the Midwest, its potential
annual destruction might well surpass the total cost of the
proud new seaway.

Once at large it builds up its population rapidly, and is
capable of making infested grain wholly useless. The khapra
is one of the numerous insects that make storage of food and
feed grains so great a problem in those tropical and semitrop-
ical countries where United States shipments go in our efforts
to alleviate their hunger problems.

Many products other than grain have to be held in storage
for varied intervals, and the spoilage hazard has to be taken
into account when the marketable items are priced. The
losses on peanuts are said to be more than $10 million a year.
While only man among vertebrates appears to contract the
tobacco habit, insects are far from immune to it; their depre-
dation on stored tobacco has been estimated at considerably
more than $15 million a year.

Wool, mohair, and similar products suffer losses in storage
that, without chemical protections, would be far greater.
Dried fruit, unless properly treated and handled, can undergo losses up to 20 per cent; these have been sharply reduced, however. Perishable stored fruits, such as apples, are
susceptible to scalds, rots, and molds, which science has been
able to eliminate or reduce so that little blemished or decayed product is ever exposed to consumers.

The manufacturing techniques now used for cleaning the

immense quantities of raw grains that are turned into flour, meal, and other food products have been made marvelously efficient. Consumers use their output without apprehension as to sanitary condition. Nevertheless, it is interesting to compare the standards exacted in this respect with those demanded for chemical residues.

The official tolerance for DDT residue is seven parts per million; for chlordane, three-tenths of one ppm.

In grain the standard of tolerance in sanitation, in effect only since 1956, is a maximum of not more than one rodent pellet per pint, or not more than one per cent per pint of insect-damaged kernels. Damaged kernels would be those partially eaten, along with such insect eggs, egg sacks, and excrement as might occur. The one per cent would be ten thousand ppm. The tolerance for rodent pellets, which vary in size between those of rats and mice, might figure out to average somewhere around 150 ppm.

This matter is not mentioned with intent to criticize either the official tolerances, which are set at what conscientious public servants find to be the lowest practicable point, nor to reflect upon the grain processors who spend huge sums to prepare their raw materials in the cleanest possible manner. It is mentioned, however, to make clear that something more than dollar losses follows when insects and rodents pursue their evil ways in the grain storages. The more perfectly their ravages can be controlled, reduced, or eliminated, the less anyone will need to be disturbed about them from any standpoint.

14/Beetle, Spare That Tree!

NEW YORK CITY, A PURPORTED SINK OF INIQUITY BLAMED by some as a source of moral blights alleged to infect the innocent remainder of the nation, may also be charged with the blight that destroyed one of America's most useful and beautiful trees. The chestnut blight was first observed in 1904 in the New York Zoological Park.

At its best a magnificent tree, an occasional chestnut grew to be a hundred feet tall, with a diameter in proportion. It was a gracious tree that fed the deer and wild turkeys, the squirrels, bears and other denizens of the wild; to say nothing of the generations of boys and girls who gathered the nuts in autumn time and shared the harvest with their parents before the winter's home fires. The wood yielded tannin to tan leather for millions of boots and shoes; furnished props for mines, poles for telegraph and telephone, ties for railroads; and supplied rail and posts for miles of sound farm fences. Chestnut wood is remarkably resistant to decay from moisture and contact with the soil. A few miles from where I write a chestnut fence still stands along the damp and shrubby border of a swamp where someone built it more than seventy-five years ago.

Within half a century the blight had killed virtually every native American chestnut tree throughout its natural range from lower Maine across New England, New York, Pennsylvania and New Jersey and had swept over some of Michigan and Ohio down into the northern parts of Alabama and Georgia.

The disease that began in the big zoo originated with a fungus native to China, Korea and Japan. Probably it came here on imported nursery material; at that time no plant quarantine officers stood guard against such undesirable aliens. To some extent the fungus also grows on red maple, shagbark hickory and upon several kinds of oaks, but among species other than chestnut it has done most damage to the valuable post oak.

Winds spread the fungus. So to a lesser extent do insects, birds, and shipments of infected materials. No practicable control for it was ever found. Here and there in the southern Appalachians a bit of chestnut forest may still be found standing; standing bare, dead, and ghostly.

Are the stately elm trees of the East and Midwest now to follow the lamented chestnut? This distressing possibility can be blamed upon the two elm bark beetles, one native and one European, which spread the Dutch elm disease. A shipment of imported logs for veneer is charged with bringing the disease here. First noticed in 1930, it has traveled as fast and even farther than did the chestnut blight. Superb elms by the thousands succumbed in New England and New York where their beauty and native vigor had long made them favorites for streets and lawns. Within twenty years the elms in Kentucky and Tennessee and even some in Colorado had been infected.

The killing fungus seems to depend solely on the beetles for its travels. The fact that these insects can fly for several miles helps to explain its rapid dissemination. The beetles breed mostly in dead elm wood and bark, but feed on the living tree. The fungus can live in either dead or healthy wood. When it reaches live wood, sap can carry it to all parts of the tree.

At first the only means to fight the Dutch elm disease was to cut and destroy all dead trees and burn all logs, twigs and bark, and all infected limbs. This is no easy task, especially when high-up dying branches have to be removed. The numerous elms growing in the semiwild state where they escape attention tend to keep the beetles and disease in business. Later, when DDT became available, an oil emulsion spray was found to be a generally effective control measure. The treatment, however, produced some chain effects. That story belongs in another chapter, as does the story of a new systemic killer of the beetle vectors.

Elms succumb easily to another disease called phloem necrosis, quite different in character, and caused by a virus instead of by a fungus. Again, an insect does the dirty work; it is a species of elm leaf hopper, also a good flier. The phloem necrosis in a number of midwestern cities has deadened thousands of once flourishing elms. DDT will subdue the necrosis where outbreaks are especially virulent.

The fight to keep the elms green and growing may be a long one; to eradicate completely the fungus, the virus, and the beetle and leaf hopper vectors, appears as yet to be an unlikely accomplishment.

We appreciate the cherished trees for both their esthetic and economic merits. A splendidly ornamental elm, beech, or other good tree enriches the enjoyment of any homestead, be it city lot or country estate, for the owners and for passersby; and it enhances the actual value. Trees add beauty to the landscape, provide shade and comfort for the body, recreation for children, homes for wildlife, and a veritable multitude of products useful and necessary to man. No one likes to know that a tree dies needlessly, whether it be in his yard, the town park, or hidden away in a distant forest.

James Truslow Adams, describing the dense primeval

forest which confronted the first American settlers, wrote in the prologue to his *Epic of America* that "a squirrel might have leaped from bough to bough for a thousand miles and never have seen a flicker of sunshine on the ground, so contiguous were the boughs and so dense the leafage."

Despite three and a half centuries of clearing and slashing, the United States can classify one of its every three acres as forest land. Half of the South, three-fourths of New England and five-sixths of the Northwest remain forest-covered or suitable only for trees. From the day the settler's first ax blow startled the quiet woods, the people have always been dependent upon wood; and we still are. Forestry and its associated works rank fourth or fifth among our industries.

The original, virgin forest supported its portion of insects, and at times combinations of conditions led to areas being devastated. But new kinds of bugs and fungi and viruses kept crossing the seas, leaving enemies behind, and finding here environments congenial to exploding their populations. More than one hundred economically important species of trees grow in our forests; and each of these, along with a thousand less valuable kinds, has its own separate bug and disease problems. More good timber is said to be destroyed each year by diseases and insects than disappears because of fires and sawmills combined. Insects alone are responsible for the loss of enough timber to build more than a million houses; and diseases enough to build two million more.

The tree grows slowly and has a comparatively long life—in some species extremely long—and at no time from sprout to maturity can it be sure to be exempt from danger. It can neither run away, scratch its wounds, nor defend itself. A single attack can murder trees that have outlived from one to a dozen generations of man to achieve their present "standings."

It was first degree murder in the forests of Colorado some two decades ago. The criminal, unfortunately, survived and remains at large. A little, cylinder-shaped, hard-shelled rascal no bigger than a housefly, he was the Engelmann spruce beetle (named after the tree, not after the excellent German-American physician and botanist for whom the tree was called).

One may still see the corpses of the victims, upright and fallen, dead, starkly leafless, in the high Rockies where once they stood green and stately. Within half a dozen years, 1942–48, enough timber for 400,000 houses had been destroyed. Across six beautiful national forests, billions of board feet of timber were uselessly ruined.

The kill is accomplished simply. The beetles bore under the bark and cut tunnels in which to place eggs; the eggs hatch and the larvae keep on digging. You have, perhaps, seen an unwanted tree girdled with an ax to cause its death before removal? The spruce beetles, just so, completely eat their girdle of death around the trunk: sap cannot move between roots and branches to exchange the nutriments of the earth for the vigor of the sunshine and air.

Writing in the 1952 Yearbook of Agriculture, N.D. Wugand, an entomologist, and Arthur L. Nelson, a forester, assessed the damage of the outbreak then in progress: "The value in standing trees is estimated at $8 million. It might some day have been made into products valued at $200 million. . . . In the six years, sixteen times more timber was destroyed than was killed by fire in the past thirty years in the Rocky Mountain region."

The same writers present the author with an occasion to quote a favorable word for his favorite family of birds. Referring to enemies of the Engelmann spruce beetles, they say: "Woodpeckers are especially effective; when they are abundant they destroy 45 to 95 per cent of the brood." As a matter of fact, woodpeckers are great consumers of pine bark beetles and numerous other forest enemies. One could wish their abundance to be greater.

The gypsy moth affords another kind of story. Nearly a hundred years ago a Frenchman figured that by crossing the

silkworm with a gypsy moth he would make himself a for-
tune. Perhaps he planned to combine the moth's voracity
with the silkworm's spinner. Anyway, he brought some gypsy
moths to Massachusetts and they escaped from his cages. The
Frenchman has been forgotten, but not the moths. They are
defoliators, which chew up the leaves of both deciduous and
evergreen trees, often denuding them completely. They kill
some trees and prevent others from making growth. Over
much of the Northeast they became so destructive that federal and state authorities for more than fifty years have
fought to subdue their ravages and delay their spread.

After DDT was found to be effective against the moth, the
official program called for spraying considerable areas with a
one-pound per acre solution of that chemical. A group of
Long Islanders in 1957 sued in federal courts to stop the
spraying. After lengthy hearings the judge denied the injunc-
tion, on the ground that the evidence introduced proved no
damage to human health and little to birds or beneficial insects.

The suit, however, raised some questions not to be ignored. When public authorities, though with the most constructive of purposes, engage in campaigns that drop sprays
over the properties of individuals who have not been consulted or have not approved, even though they may have
been notified of the plans, certainly some degree of invasion
into the rights of privacy occurs. Not only the gypsy-moth
efforts, but those to destroy the fire ant and the Mediterranean fruit fly involve the same principle. The decision to
spray, however well meant, is a bureaucratic decision; no
substantial harm may follow the program; it may accomplish
its desirable purpose. A really dire emergency might justify
such action. Nevertheless an individual's front and back yards
and his swimming pool are parts of his castle, and one may
well argue against the right of government forces to invade
them by aerial sprays or other means.

Despite the abundant ignorance science still confesses

about countless species, a vast amount of entomological lore has been accumulated. The interested person who wants to probe deeper into the ways of bugs than this simple volume will take him will have to look elsewhere, for we do not propose to impose upon our readers more than a fair glimpse of a few of the innumerable six- eight- and more-legged arthropods and their legless relatives. These glimpses, we hope, will be enough to persuade the doubtful that, although not all risks have been eliminated, they are few enough, and that the need for the wise use of pesticides is so overwhelming that until better tools can be devised, we should judiciously employ those we now have; meanwhile striving to improve them, to improve their uses, and to learn better how to balance our gains and hazards.

We shall accordingly spare the details about the vast devastation wrought in public and private forests by the spruce budworm, the hemlock looper, the pine tussock moth, the five-spined ips beetle, the Saratoga spittle beetle, the white pine blister rust and the black turpentine beetle, and say nothing about the scores of others that impair the beauty of the woods and occasionally destroy our none too great reserves of good timber.

The 240 million Americans expected to be here a short fifteen years from now, and the many more millions to follow them, will have little use for so many bugs. But they will need the trees, so they can build and furnish houses, make ball bats for their Little Leaguers, and enjoy the shade, beauty, and wildlife.

15/Guerrillas of the Underground

THE SHARP-EYED GARDENER, AS HE LIFTS THE SEASON'S first spade load of soil, sees more than a few pounds of inert clay and loam. He salutes the wriggling earthworm and wonders again which, if either, is the head end. His mind may wander a bit toward a certain spot where the fishing is easier than he expects the gardening to be. He knows, of course, that this squirming hermaphrodite is a friend, devoted to improving their mutually owned soil as trifles of decayed vegetation and particles of earth pass through its segmented body.

More doubtfully he notes the white larva that, in this juvenile form, may be expecting to begin a premature harvest of garden plant growth, or planning later as a shining Japanese beetle to pollute his rose petals. Yet he may be little aware of a score of other forms whose surreptitious activities bode ill for the success of his efforts.

Out on the farm, the springtime plowman, when he turns in his tractor seat to check the depth and straightness of his furrows, is reminded that his season's work may be frustrated in part by hostile underground movements. The iridescent blackbird in his wake stabs into the newly upturned earth and gobbles grubs and worms and perhaps exposed clusters of insect eggs. If the man's fields are anywhere near the sea an acre or so of gulls will be feasting on the fresh game the plows and harrows have turned up.

Neither the grackles nor the gulls will find more than a tiny fraction of the subterranean life that hibernates and waits patiently for the spring sun's light and warmth to stir young plants to growing and to sending tender roots down for their consumption as they advance from infantile and juvenile stages to adult. And some of that life is deeper down, invisible or nearly so, and menacing.

Let's say the farmer, having plowed and harrowed and smoothed his field, has planted corn. He looks forward to long, straight, waving rows, "knee-high by the Fourth of July," and to an October harvest rich with abundant feed to make steaks and chops, milk and eggs. Once the seed is planted the underground hazards begin. The seed-corn maggot, newly hatched from the eggs its fly laid, or the seed-corn beetle, already adult, may bore into the grains and prevent their germination. Big white grubs, which eat nothing but roots and thrive on corn roots, are down there, where they may have been for two or three years before getting up courage to put on their armor and emerge as common, blundering June bugs. Three other kinds of corn rootworms, also juvenile beetle forms, have a fondness for the useful plant that gives them a distinguishing name. Worse yet are the wireworms. Sometimes so numerous as to destroy a whole stand of corn or any crop, they mature into click beetles. The cutworms are systematic; they go down a row, after the green shoots unfold to the sun, and sever each plant a bit below the surface.

Not all the damage done by these and by their dozens of accomplices will immediately become visible. Root injuries prepare the way for bacterial diseases that weaken the corn's growth. Enfeebled and deadened roots fail to collect the nutrients the plant needs, and in the pride of youth its vigor fails. Along comes a big wind or a heavy rainstorm, and the stalks topple to the ground.

For every crop and in every agricultural area, underground pests such as these spend their hidden lives damaging crops, reducing yields, gnawing away farmers' profits, and subtracting from human food supplies. The ordinary ones are well known, their life cycles familiar, and when their depredations become too serious the farmer can fumigate the soil with one of the effective chemicals, or assail the pests at some other stage of their careers.

More mysterious, often more costly, and far more difficult to deal with, another form of hostile life lurks in the soil depths from which it never climbs into the sun. Throughout the United States and probably most of the agricultural world this enemy exists. Only in recent years have its names been heard outside the recondite circles of science. But as its once secret inroads have become evident and have been identified on a score of important crops, this minute, serpentlike, long-hidden marauder begins to achieve prominence in its own department of infamy.

Every housewife cooks her pork dishes thoroughly, and probably knows why she does. She does it to protect the family against the possibility of becoming infected with trichinosis. The trichina is an almost invisible worm, which makes its way into the muscles and intestines of hogs, man and other animals. When it does manage to lodge in the human system, the illness that follows is a most unpleasant one and may become most serious.

The trichina is but one of a very numerous class of worms, most of them nearly microscopic, that infest both plants and animals. Not insects, they are nematodes. The trichina, the hookworm, and the worm that causes filariasis are nematodes, as is the organism that causes "gapes," a common ailment usually fatal to young chickens.

Along in the 1920's a new trouble was noticed in the citrus groves around Winter Haven, Florida. The trees seemed to wilt quickly in dry periods and began to appear stunted. The leaves were thin and yellowish. The fruit was smaller than normal and the yields fell off. The condition advanced little by little from one infected tree to others nearby. No one knew the cause. For want of a better name it was called "spreading decline."

Not until thirty years later were researchers able to identify the culprit. It was a microscopic, eel-like creature about one-fortieth of an inch long, the burrowing nematode. By making its way into the tiny feeder roots of the tree it sapped their life and left them to decay from fungi and bacteria. After exhausting the tissues and plant juices of one root the nematode moves to another, little by little depriving the tree of its ability to bring its nutrients and moisture up out of the soil.

More than 7,500 acres of Florida's commercial citrus groves have been infested. By itself the nematode travels slowly, seldom more than fifty feet in a year. Man has hastened the spread with his cultivating equipment, by transporting infested plant material and soil; movement of drainage water may help. Once a tree has been infected nothing now known can be done to save it.

"Push and treat" has been adopted as one method to check the burrowing nematode. After an infected area has been marked off it is surrounded by a chemical barrier in the soil to stop further spread. Then, as trees grow unprofitable they are bulldozed down and burned, and the land is treated to destroy the nematodes in the soil and in broken root pieces. New planting is considered to be safe after two yearly inspections have found the soil to be cleansed.

The same nematode attacks some 150 different ornamental plants. Florida laws impose strict regulations upon distribution of nursery stock to prevent its spread to new areas.

Meanwhile scientists are hoping to find a way to save infested trees without destroying them, or cheaper control methods, or root stocks that will resist the present costly consequences of nematode voracity.

On Long Island, and in the United States only there, the golden nematode has naturalized itself in the famed potato fields. First recognized in Germany about 1890, it is a serious pest in much of Europe and has been located in Mexico and Peru. The name comes from the color of the globular cyst in which the female packages her numerous eggs. One cyst may contain five hundred eggs and the eggs may lie in the ground for as long as seventeen years before they decide to hatch. The nematode itself is too small for the eye to detect, but the cysts, although several can find room on a pinhead, can be seen.

Not until the golden nematode has secretly multiplied into an abundant infestation does its presence become easily apparent, because no immediate sign shows on the top growth of potato or tomato plants. The worm by itself can move only inches a year. But in time the farmer notices that growth is being stunted on a widening area and his yield is falling off. One heavily infested piece, for instance, yielded only 15 per cent of normal.

While efforts are being made to eradicate the golden nematode from its yet small territory, or check it, the primary concern is to prevent its escape to new places. Soil fumigation with chemicals provides good control. When shipments come from foreign countries federal quarantine inspectors eye them closely for cysts that may cling to straw, bags or soil. Restrictions have been placed on sales of crops, nursery stock, and topsoil from infested land. Farmers are warned to see that their workers do not carry the cysts on shoes or in trouser cuffs, and that necessary farm operations do not spread them to new ground.

Another nematode with large potentials for damage was

found in the United States for the first time a little more than ten years ago. This one is called the soybean cyst nematode. It appeared in North Carolina, having arrived from where no one knows, but since then it appears to have acquired naturalization papers at least in Missouri, Tennessee, and Arkansas. Roots of soybeans appear to be the favorite diet, although it has been found on snap beans, lespedeza, and vetch. Soybean yields on infested fields have been so little that farmers have not bothered to harvest. The worm is a bit larger than some others, the larva, adult, and cyst all being visible, though just barely. No controls have yet been found other than not planting on infested acres any known host of the nematode and taking great care that no cyst-bearing soil is carried to a new place.

The sugar beet nematode, either longer established or less exclusively inclined than its golden and citrus cousins, has spread over fifteen or more states, all west of the Mississippi except Wisconsin and Michigan. Nor does it confine its dishonorable intentions to the sugar beet; among its hosts are broccoli, Brussels sprouts, cabbage, cauliflower, Chinese cabbage, collards, kale, mangel-wurzel, radish, rape, rhubarb, spinach, Swiss chard, table beet, tomato, and turnip. An equal number of weeds affords it room and board on occasion. Nematocides will hold the pest back long enough to grow a sugar beet crop, but the expensive treatment has to be repeated each year. Rotation of fields into different, nonhost crops and other cultural practices are recommended as the most practicable controls.

The nematodes can boast of world-wide family connections, not all of them so tiny as the species we deal with here. Indeed, a relative in the Asiatic tropics is reputed to grow to be a yard long. Nor are all kinds so choosy about their food plants. As least three have the tobacco habit: the root knot, meadow, and stunt nematodes. The first two of those, plus the stubby root and sting species, attack cotton roots. Strawberries contend with several kinds. Nor are all nematodes "bad" from the human viewpoint. Certain species are parasitic on insects.

Whether these underground dwellers can ever be eradicated from their status as serious pests remains questionable. No reason exists not to expect that new species will appear here, or not to expect that depredations will become troublesome in crops where their presence has not so far been evident. A general necessity to purchase and apply nematocides to fumigate soils would add a huge cost to agricultural production. While shifting crops and adjusting cultural practices can usually reduce nematode damage in field crops, the ability of the cysts to live several years while awaiting a favorable bounty certainly encourages little hope for cultural eradication.

The menace is realized, however, as new species and new outbreaks have come to light. The chemists and other scientists have accepted the challenge.

The virus and bacterial diseases that share with nematodes and soil insects in the subterranean campaign against successful crop production form still another important alliance in the opposition. Science each year learns more about them, and with more knowledge will be able to devise better artillery for the campaigns against them.

16/Weeds, and a
Terrible Beast

WEEDS ARE NOT BUGS, BUT THEY ARE PESTS, AND CHEMI-cals are used to combat them. The adventurous reader who has traveled so far as to reach this page may enjoy a slight change of scene. So herein we shall briefly consider unwanted plants and why hundreds of them are so pestiferous, and shall mention several marvelous new methods for fighting them. This will be preceded by several paragraphs of personal reminiscence, garrulous but pertinent. Before the chapter concludes we shall also introduce, for want of another appropriate place to mention him, the world's most dangerous animal, wild or tame.

No one ever had to convince this writer that weeds were pests, for they pestered his summers through all the years of his Ohio farm boyhood. When school adjourned Father was likely to hand me a sharp hoe and lead the way to the cornfield; he was not a man to ask his boy to do something he would not himself do.

At that time the hoe was our best weed killer. A hoe, if anyone present has no clear idea of its nature, is a steel blade, usually about eight inches long and half as wide, firmly attached at right angles to a handle a little thicker than a broomstick and a foot or more longer. In those days, at least, the handle was usually made from tough hickory, which was almost impossible to break by any accident a boy could contrive. The hoe is operated by muscle power.

The hoe was probably the most monotonous farm tool ever invented. There were really only two things one could do with it. One was to draw the blade forcefully and quickly just under the soil surface. This action severed weeds from their roots; repeated every few seconds for ten hours, the motion killed many weeds. The other thing one could do was to place the rounded upper end of the handle under the armpit and lean. This broke the monotony for a bit, but never seemed to elicit any favorable comment.

One defect in the hoe was that, except in the winter months when one went to school anyway, it never really went out of season. The weeds arose with the first warmth of spring and kept on rising until the sun had retreated to the southern hemisphere in the fall.

Besides the hoe we had other weedicides. After a heavy rain, when the cornfields and garden were too muddy for hoeing, one could go into the oats field and pull mustard by hand. That was wet work, but the mustard pulled with little effort and the bright yellow blossoms made the weed easy to find. Since one mustard plant consumes as much soil nutrient as four oat plants, its removal was desirable. When the mustard was exhausted and other wet mornings occurred, one could go to the hayfields and pull sour dock, which was not so pretty and resisted muscular lifting.

Father remarked occasionally that one of his ambitions was to round out a year in which no weed on our farm had been allowed to go to seed. He never quite achieved the goal. His fence rows were cleaned by the scythe, and no mullein or thistle was permitted to mature seed in the blue grass pasture. But the late weeds, those that sprang up around Labor Day and after, always defeated his purpose because from then on the demands of corn harvest and wheat sowing deflected all hands from weedicidal pursuits. When he read in a farmer's bulletin that some weed seeds can remain viable in the soil for thirty years or more before conditions induce them to sprout I thought he was disturbed, but he was not discouraged.

Corn was the most important crop and the one most vulnerable to the competition from weeds. After a field was plowed the two-horse spike-tooth harrow crossed as many times as possible; each harrowing exposed new weed sprouts upon which the sun at this juncture performed fatally as a weedicide. After planting the boy continued harrowing until the new corn stalks were up three or four inches. The next weedicide to come into action was the horse-drawn, wheeled cultivator whose gang shovels stirred the soil, killed the weeds between rows, and covered some of those in the rows. This device took one row at a time (multiple-row cultivators came later) and had a great advantage. One could ride on it. However, because it occasionally covered up a corn plant, and because it could not reach all the weeds in the rows, the war on weeds required that someone, preferably a boy, follow along with the hoe to chop out the escapees and release the smothered corn plants.

Before midsummer the cultivator was expected to have made three complete passes over the corn fields and the stalks were expected to have grown too high to permit further use of that machine. So the crop was "laid by" in late June or early July and all attention turned to the hay and small-grain harvests.

The respite for the hoe and the hoer, however, was temporary. While golden tassels emerged atop the fast-growing stalks, and below them ears began shooting outward and forming their silky tips, a new crop of weeds disputed ground with the corn. Pigweed, lamb's-quarters and others could grow a yard high in a few short weeks, with root bases so tough that only a really sharp hoe's hard strokes could lay them flat.

In late summer or early fall we had another weed-killing job that was easy. The young clover and new grass seedings were getting started in the stubble where the wheat and oats had been harvested; but ragweed and its associates were starting faster. So we clipped those fields with the mowing machine and thereafter under the mild fall sun the clovers and timothy came along sturdily.

Father, of course, was entirely right in pursuing his determined war on weeds; or almost entirely. With deep roots and many underground fibers some weed species do loosen and aerate the soil and leave in it some useful organic matter. But they compete ceaselessly with the crops for soil nutrients. They steal moisture. They shut off light. They clog harvesting equipment. They lessen the feed value of hay and forage. They impair the quality of food and fiber crops. They adulterate harvested grains. They harbor plant-disease organisms and insect pests.

Now the new chemical herbicides can reduce tremendously the labor once required to control weeds. They have many desirable qualities. At the usual rates of application they do not injure animals, fish, or men. They do not damage useful soil organisms. Small doses, frequently less than a pound per acre of the active ingredient, accomplish their purpose. No accumulation in the soil follows their judicious use. The application methods are simple. Being selective, they kill the principal weed pests, which are mostly broadleaf plants, without injuring grasses and grain.

Intriguing names for some widely used herbicides are diuron, semagine, amiben, dalapon, 2,4-D, 2,4,5-T, Silvex, MCPA, and 4-(2,4-DB). These terms, of course, are abbreviations of the full names; the complete name of Silvex, for example, if you prefer not to use an abbreviation, is 2-(2,4,5-trichlorophenoxy) propionic acid.

They do their jobs quite simply. On contact the chemical moves quickly through leaves, stems, and roots, and the plant dies. If the herbicide is sprayed on the soil, the roots absorb and spread it.

For row crops, such as the corn that once demanded weeks of cultivation and hoeing to restrain the weeds, pre-emergence sprays perform effectively. Seeds of the principal row crops usually are planted from a half-inch to two inches below the surface. If the field is sprayed after planting but before the crop seeds emerge, weed trouble is greatly reduced. Postemergence spraying, usually cheaper and more convenient, is much more widely used.

The herbicides will kill weeds in pastures and on range land, along irrigation and drainage ditches, highway and railroad rights of way, under power lines, as well as in lawns and gardens. Some 75 million acres of cropland are sprayed annually.

The importance of the chemical weed controls can be appreciated fully only by those with enough farm background to be familiar with the prevalence of weeds, their persistence, and their capacity for competing successfully with crops—and by those who know something of the laborious efforts by which generations of farmers have fought with weeds to be able to raise their crops.

Every state long ago adopted laws to prevent inclusion of noxious weed seeds in crop seeds offered for sale. Many states also have laws that penalize farmers who permit certain especially pernicious weeds to grow where they may spread to other farms. Seventy years ago, the 1895 *Yearbook of Agriculture* listed two hundred weed species as serious obstacles to profitable farming. Of these, 108 had been introduced from other countries, and a few more have arrived since. The seeds are usually small and may pass undetected even after the best efforts to separate them. Only two pints of clover seeds brought from England in 1860 were reported to have contained 70,000 weed seeds. A recent USDA *Farmer's Bulletin* (No. 2183) lists more than 450 plants as weeds and records the response of each to various chemical controls.

USDA scientists estimate that $5 billion for each year, 1951–1960, would hardly cover the losses caused by weeds to American agriculture in reduced yield and quality of crops and costs of control.

The California State Chamber of Commerce concluded a few years ago that weeds were imposing an entirely unacceptable burden upon the people and upon the state's economy. A Statewide Weed Control Committee was established in 1956, with J. Earl Coke, a vice president of the state's biggest banking system, as chairman. The committee estimates that the annual cost of weeds and control measures exceeds $370 million in California. It notes, also, that only about 15/100 of one per cent of that amount is spent on research to find better ways to meet the problem.

One of the committee's interesting contributions is a definition of weeds:

> Weeds are insidious thieves; they are robbers of water, of light, of nutrients, and often of natural beauty. They are carriers of pathogenic pests, feeders of fires. They are legion in number, numerous in kinds, variable in habit, often poisonous in character. They are restless travelers that freely enter and tenaciously hold sites whose plants have been exploited or foolishly neglected by man. Weeds are crafty enemies, without senses, without mercy; they lurk everywhere throughout the civilized world and move about quietly, unobtrusively, in seemingly endless variety. Weeds are successful competitors; that is why we generally define them as "plants out of place" or "unwanted" plants.

Despite their relative harmlessness, as with any chemicals the weed killers must be used with some precautions. The man with the handsprayer who attempts to kill off the poison ivy from his back lot should never forget that a bit of breeze could carry a few drops lethal to the neighbor's rose garden. Comparable precautions are observed in the fields when susceptible plants may be within range.

The weedicides have not achieved perfection. Farmers report that they vary in effectiveness from poor, fair, good, to excellent. They do greatly reduce the manpower and machine-hour requirements. In addition to the weedicides named above, several dozen others have been developed, many of them highly selective. Industrial and publicly supported scientists actively seek improvements in compounds, formulations, application techniques, and new fundamental knowledge to extend usefulness.

Aside from herbicides, other chemicals will play big new parts as man shapes up the future of growing things.

Among crops, defoliants have already established a place. Defoliation of cotton reduces the amount of trash that reaches the gin and increases the ease and completeness of machine picking. In certain seed crops defoliants have found uses.

Whatever one may hear about things that have been done with gibberellic acid, it is almost certain to create a degree of speculative excitement. It is a growth stimulant. For instance, a black walnut sprout that normally would grow a foot and a half in a year was induced to grow eight and a half feet. So far the only extensive commercial application has been on Thompson seedless grapes in California, where it improves the size of the fruit. Gibberellic acid was first derived from a Japanese rice fungus. Experiments continue to test the stuff on scores of plant species.

Chemical retardants to achieve opposite effects are creating deep interest; these are dwarf makers. Success at shortening flower stems, as of chrysanthemums, has been considerable. Experiments at modifying field crops, such as soybeans, are under way. Most likely the early uses will apply to flowers and ornamental plants.

Other growth regulators have become well established. In thousands of acres of orchards a few grams per acre prevent the fruits, especially apples and pears, from dropping prematurely. Pineapples in Hawaii and Puerto Rico are helped to flower earlier and to produce uniform fruit by a spray, at exactly the right time, of a low 2,4-D concentration. And after thinking of this and other phenoxy preparations as plant killers, it is interesting to learn that a little bit of 2,4,5-T will cause cuttings of certain rhododrendron varieties to root much more readily.

The world's most dangerous beast to man boasts no formidable size. His weight can be measured in ounces and his length in inches. Neither the roaring tiger nor the slinking cobra can exceed him in deeds of evil. His name is rat.

At his worst the rat carries fleas which bear the infection of typhus and bubonic plague. Paul Friggens in *Reader's Digest* (January, 1965) said, ". . . it is estimated that around the world this disease-carrying rodent has killed more people than all the wars in history."

In the United States the rat's worst is not his most. Feeding and crawling among stores of food and grain, leaving behind him hairs, urine, and feces, each rat contaminates or consumes twenty to twenty-five dollars' worth of foodstuffs a year. Considering that his numbers probably equal the human population, the USDA says that this destruction is equivalent to the output of 100,000 average farms.

If rats were able to breed unchecked, how many might infest this land of plenty could become an exercise in mathematics. With the ability to produce a litter every twenty-two days, one pair could boast a posterity of 1,500 within one year.

As many as ten thousand lice were reported to have been

found on a single rat; and besides lice and fleas the beasts also distribute mites. In city tenement houses, rats have been known to gnaw helpless babies. With sharp, fast-growing incisor teeth the rat gnaws persistently at wood, metal, or concrete; he will chew the insulation from electric wires, thus occasionally adding arson to his other crimes.

Besides being a ferocious and savage criminal, the rat learns quickly to avoid traps and ordinary dangers. His wariness is remarkable. The prewar rodent poisons such as red squill (a bulb from Mediterranean countries) and strychnine killed relatively few of his kind; once a member of his colony suspected that a bait had sickened him the others avoided it.

Not until after World War Two did any weapon appear that offered real promise against the rat. A Wisconsin farmer found his cows dying for no apparent reason. When he sought help from the state college of agriculture, Dr. Karl Paul Link investigated. He watched cows die while eating peacefully and comfortably to the end. The cause was found in spoiled sweet clover which formed a chemical called dicoumarin. An anticoagulant, it brought about painless internal hemorrhages. Link observed that it not only killed rats but that they showed little suspicion of it. This led him to develop a product called Warfarin. He assigned the patent to the Wisconsin Alumni Research Foundation, which licensed formulators who gave it national distribution. Peculiarly, rats would eat it mixed with a corn meal bait even when placed in a corn crib. For the first time a means had appeared that promised the elimination of rats from any area where people were determined to be rid of them, and millions of rats were killed. Warfarin is also effective for mice, and is easy to place so that other animals are not affected.

More recently, a still more specific rat killer has been placed on the market. It doesn't even kill mice. Researchers in a pharmaceutical house, McNeil Laboratories, were hunting for a product that would help the victims of arthritis. One that didn't work was then checked as a drug for diet control. Again it didn't work, but the experimenter discovered that it promptly killed rats, yet did no harm to mice or any other animals. The active compound has been named Norbormide and in prepared bait form is marketed under a trade mark as Raticate. A phenomenal effectiveness has been reported by grain storages, pest control operators, and farmers.

Objectionable rats come in several species. The Norway rat prevails in the United States, although the roof rat appears in southern areas. The black rat and the Alexandrine rat are among the world species. Wherever rats prosper they go, even, as is well known, on voyages by ships to different lands. A world-wide eradication campaign against rats could be profitable in terms of health and property and a blessing to the human race. Nothing whatever can be said in favor of the beasts.

17/Nourishment Before Harvest

ON ONE OF ALABAMA'S GLOWING SPRING MORNINGS NEARLY forty years ago I stood beside Dr. George Washington Carver, the famous Negro chemist and educator, at a bench in his simple Tuskegee laboratory. He had just shown me samples of the 202 different products he had at that time made from peanuts.

He gave me an elegantly simple lesson in chemistry.

"How did you go about it to make all these things out of peanuts?" I asked him.

"Why, I just took a handful of peanuts and looked at them, and I said, 'Great Creator, *why* did you make the peanut? Why?'

"Then, with such knowledge as I had of chemistry and physics I set to work to take the peanut apart. I separated the water, the fats, the oils, the gums, the resins, sugars, starches, pectoses, pentoses, pentosans, legumen, lysin, the amino and amido acids.

"There! I had all the parts of the peanut spread out before me."

Almost everyone understands analysis, or what it means. There it was. He had taken the peanut apart.

"Then I merely went on to try different combinations of those parts, under different conditions of temperature, pressure, and so forth.

"The result was what you see—these 202 different products, all made from peanuts."

First the analysis, then the synthesis. He put the parts back together, but under different conditions and in different combinations. Dr. Carver's shoe polish, dyes, lotions and 199 other items were still peanuts, put together differently than before. So they were natural in inner character, albeit synthetic in composition. The perfect antonym for analysis is synthesis.

The word *synthetic* long ago acquired an unfortunate "image." To the public mind it denoted "artificial" at a time when man's efforts to improve upon nature were far less successful than later. Thirty years ago rayon, a synthetic or artificial fiber, had its place but it was not so good as cotton, wool or silk. It was made from wood pulp, the same basic material as newsprint; paper was not thought of as synthetic, though it was, after all, an artificial product and a much better one for practical purposes than vellum from sheepskin. Though you didn't have to send it to the laundry, the celluloid collar was not quite so satisfactory as a linen one.

Now we hardly ask whether our automobile tires are made from natural or from synthetic rubber, or whether the cord in them is cotton, rayon, or nylon. A plastic item frequently suits us better than its metal or glass counterpart. Our abundant "miracle" drugs are synthetic, and when they are needed we rejoice to have them.

In this sort of indifference to origin any member of the plant kingdom was far ahead of the rest of us.

To fulfill its destiny the sprouting seed sends roots down into the soil in search of nutrients and moisture, and puts its leaves into the air to absorb its needs of carbon, oxygen and hydrogen. When the rootlet reaches a trace of suitable food it never asks whether that minuscule bit had waited there for a century, whether it came lately from barn stable manure or from a chemical fertilizer. To the plant's future those mites of underground nourishment are vital. While the analogy may be fetched a bit far, one might say that what the plant absorbs from the soil provides the basic power for its above-ground achievement. That battery is below.

This seems strange when measured against the surprising fact that up to 98 per cent of nearly all plant substance—be it geranium, corn stalk or tall pine—actually derives from air and moisture, with sunshine as the battery above ground. The portion that is taken from the soil is represented by what ash remains when the plant is burned.

What does the plant need that it searches for in the soil?

Chemical substances! Chemicals that give it power to send up a strong stem, to put out vigorous leaves and sound blossoms that will mature into healthy fruit and seeds, the essentials for the future reproduction of its kind.

In virgin soils untouched by man the substances occurring in the soil determine the kinds of vegetation that grow there naturally. Marsh reeds and grasses do not rise from a hillside, nor do the upland plants grow in the swamp.

The farmer long ago discovered that when he attempted to grow the same crop on the same field year after year he could expect the yields to decline. The land, he said, was worn out, exhausted. Erosion by wind and water produced this effect as well as repeated crops: the end result was about the same. His crop plants could no longer find in the soil the food elements essential to vigorous growth. To some extent he could repair this deficiency by spreading manure and plowing under other organic matter. When the bacterial and chemical activities under the surface had converted this material into suitable inorganic plant nutrients the crop improved again.

Until about the last fifteen years of his life my father was what would now be called an organic farmer. He sold virtually none of his grain and hay. Each fall he shipped in car-loads of cattle or lambs to which the produce of the fields was fed. He grew and fattened hogs. Horses furnished the draft power, cows supplied our milk, and a hundred or so chickens gave us meat and eggs.

"The only fertility that leaves our farm," he often said, "is what goes away after it has been wrapped up in the hide of a fat animal."

Straw from the small grains and the corn stalks all passed into the stables for bedding. Whenever time and conditions permitted we hauled manure. Scores of loads were piled into the spreader and scattered over the fields. Since there never was enough, even with the numbers of livestock, to cover all the acres, the fields nearest to the barn received the most frequent treatment.

"Even if we don't always make money by fattening stock," Father said, "I figure that the manure they make pays for the extra labor they require."

While our farm was not a large one, Father employed a full-time hired man. "The winter feeding work makes it pos-sible to keep a man profitably employed the year around," he explained. Another point, not pertinent here, was that with a man always on the job he could get away for an occasional vacation or outing. He was a wise man in his time.

An "outing" might be a visit to the state experiment sta-tion. He read its bulletins faithfully. When, despite all the livestock fed and all the organic matter returned to the soil, yields from even the best fields failed to increase and actually declined, he knew what to do. He knew that the plant rootlets were not finding all they needed. For the first time on our farm and I believe for the first time in the neigh-borhood, an application of commercial fertilizer, high in phosphate, was drilled along with the wheat. The wheat yield next summer was the best the farm had ever known, and the mixed hay crop that followed showed clear improvement.

Father never ceased to feed animals and to spread every possible load of manure. But he was no longer just an organic farmer. He added the commercial fertilizers.

The many tons of manure gave our soil a little something more than the few chemical constituents to which the subsurface processes eventually reduced them. They improved its physical condition, kept it more friable, better able to retain moisture, better suited in general to encourage root growth. Tilth, we called those qualities. Probably they made it easier for the organic materials to release the tiny trifles of nitrogen, phosphorus or potassium into inorganic form so that the plant roots could absorb them. Probably they also made the commercial fertilizer elements more available.

Even though only live animals, wool, a little butter and a few eggs were sold from our farm, soil depletion occurred. They carried away with them fertility elements amounting, according to latter day authorities, to a fifth or more of what the crops consumed.

Tons of soil elements vanish from farms everywhere into the seas each year by way of drainage and through city sewage discharges. The huge food shipments we send overseas, whether for dollars or for mercy, take along with them a toll of essential soil elements which farmers must replace to maintain their yields.

Scientists will admit that they do not yet know as much as they hope to learn about the mysterious biological and chemical affairs that take place in the hidden underfarm. But they do know a great deal about plant requirements. Since Justus von Liebig's great experiments a century and a quarter ago, scientists in a hundred experiment stations here and many others abroad have checked repeatedly in field and laboratory to learn how plants respond to what they are fed. They are not guessing when they report on the relationship between what the soil contains and how the plant performs. They know that if the manure the farmer plows under contains nitrogen or phosphorus, some potassium, calcium, magnesium, or other plant elements, the subterranean chemical factories will in time put them in shape for use by a plant. They know that if a farmer buys the same elements in fertilizer, the same result will follow. The plant rejoices and grows; it doesn't ask who brought the dinner nor whence it came.

For maximum growth the plant must have soil in the physical condition its particular species prefers, access to the air and moisture from which, with the sun's aid, it turns carbon, hydrogen, and oxygen into its substance, and in the soil a correct balance of the chemical elements it desires. Primarily it asks the soil for nitrogen, phosphorus and potassium, and secondarily for calcium, magnesium and sulphur. Then, depending upon the particular soil and climate, it may need boron, copper, iron, manganese, molybdenum, zinc, and chlorine. These latter may be required in extremely slight quantities—a mere trace of molybdenum can make the difference between a poor alfalfa crop and a fine one—but the complete absence of any of these can cause failure, even with all other elements sufficiently available. As does the human body, the plant wants a balanced diet.

These elements, in scores of combinations and grades, are prepared by the fertilizer manufacturers and are purchased by farmers all over the United States to improve their lands and increase their crops. The 1964 usage was almost ten million tons of primary nutrients (or thirty million tons of chemical fertilizers). Without them our abundance would be lessened; and since health depends in large part upon what people eat, our well-being has its own relation to the use of the so-called "artificial" fertilizers.

No part of our planet earth has been less altered by human hand, made to become less unnatural, than the bottoms of the seas. There the debris from uncounted millennia of organic life has accumulated. Lives of the sea organisms are mortal; from whales to plankton, their carcasses disintegrate and subside into the depths.

Upheavals and changes through the eons have caused the

seas from time to time to shift their dominions. Ancient sea
bottoms in Florida, Tennessee, and Idaho, covered now by
other deposits, today yield up phosphate rock left there from
primordial times. The coastal region of North Carolina, re-
coverable undersea nodules off the California coast, and spots
in Montana, Utah, and North Africa also are phosphate
sources.

In New Mexico near Carlsbad, in south California, in
Utah and Saskatchewan, departing seas and subsequent geological events left accessible deposits of potassium, now being
mined for fertilizer uses.

By weight the atmosphere is around three-fourths nitrogen. Overhead flow limitless supplies of this element, some
35,000 tons over every acre of land. Leguminous plants have
always known how to bring it down and how to leave some of
it in the soil. That's why farmers have esteemed clovers and
alfalfas as soil-building crops. Now chemical processes pull
nitrogen out of the air, or produce it from coal or petroleum,
where the air and vegetation had to do with its original depo-
sition.

From such natural sources the modern fertilizer industry
extracts and formulates the varied preparations that feed
America's crops. The roots push down from the corn and
wheat and vegetable seeds, down from the fruit trees, and
find there that nature's processes have prepared the nutrients
that create growth. As we said earlier, they do not ask
whether the goodies had long been there, came lately from
buried manures, or were bought for them from factories. The
elements are the same, and only when they are the same can
they nourish life in plants, plants that in turn nourish animals and human beings.

Can they be injurious? Poisons as well as nutriments exist
throughout nature. Not all plants are safely edible. Loco
weed poisons animals; so at certain stages will the leaves of
the common wild cherry tree. Man avoids the deadly kinds of

mushrooms. But no evidence whatever has ever indicated that any edible plant fails in nutritive value, or bears any injurious ingredient, because it has fed on nitrogen, phosphorus, potassium or micronutrients compounded into fertilizers required for the most profitable plant growth.

For more than a century chemical elements, in ever increasing quantities, have supplemented the organic manures and plant residues to improve our crops. A century ago in this country, life expectancy at birth was little more than forty years; now it has risen to threescore and ten. While many factors have contributed to this, surely if eating fertilized crops is bad for people, something other than emotional and theoretical evidence would long ago have been established.

The idea of "organic farming" has attracted numbers of people. Many of them are enthusiastically articulate. They insist that only "natural" methods should be employed in food production, meaning cultivation, use of manures and composts, and such means as completely avoid the application of fertilizers, sprays or additives in any "artificial" forms. A measure of good has resulted from their theories in that they have directed increased attention to some of the soil's biological aspects.

One of the criteria harped upon by organic advocates has been the earthworm population, which they have assumed to be indicative of soil health. One of the world's foremost soils scientists, long chairman of the New Jersey Experiment Station soils department and editor of *Soil Science,* an internationally accepted scientific journal, looked into the matter. This authority, Dr. Firman E. Bear, reported:

> On the New Jersey Experiment Station, a plot of limed land was planted to *Lespedeza sericea* (a kind of clover). It received a 1,000 pound application of 0-12-12 fertilizer per acre at seeding time and 500 pounds per acre every year for the next five years.

On the 6th of November, 1946, the number of earthworms in the top six inches of soil on that plot was
1,200,000 per acre, with an additional 90,000 in the
second six inches, and 30,000 more in the third six
inches. Earthworms are no more sensitive to fertilizer
than are the root hairs of plants. If temporarily disturbed by an overdose, a worm can move but the root
hair can't. In general, the heavier the application of
fertilizer, within limits, the greater the growth of
crops and the larger amount of crop residues that
are left behind in the soil. These provide food for the
earthworms.

At the famous Rothamsted station in England certain plots
have never received fertilizers, while others have been treated
year after year for more than a century with "artificial"
plant foods. The numbers of earthworms in each are about
the same, but in the fertilized grounds the worms are bigger
and healthier.

Several years ago, while editor of *Farm Journal,* the author
promoted what was called the "Three-Hundred-Bushel Corn
Adventure." Not a contest, it encouraged advanced farmers
to try to create optimum conditions for what, at the beginning, seemed to be an improbable yield. The record at the
outset was 191 bushels per acre. We were told by some pretty
able scientists, among others, that if such a high yield as three
hundred bushels were ever reached the corn would be defi-
cient in protein feeding value. Of course, the farmers who
participated applied ample amounts of nitrogen and other
fertilizers. The three-hundred-bushel mark was surpassed,
after nine years of the "adventure," by Lamar Ratliff, a Mississippi 4-H Club boy, from whose acre officials measured 304
bushels of Number 2 corn reduced to 15½ per cent moisture.
I don't recall that his crop was analyzed, but a previous high
adventurer, Ben Courtwright of Illinois, had marked up
256.9 bushels per acre. Corn from this acre was found to
contain 9.38% protein. The protein content of the same va-

riety in another, lower-yielding field was 8.64%. Apparently the heavy doses of nitrogen and other elements increased the protein content.

Efforts to follow strictly organic methods, though uneconomical, may succeed partially, especially if the soil is fairly good and if neighboring farmers keep their pests under control. General adherence to organic methods now, however, would fall far short of producing the abundant quantities and fine qualities of the foodstuffs American agriculture provides to consumers. All the available manures, all the crop wastes and all the roots left to decay would be far insufficient to feed the crops man needs.

In a sense it may be said that millions, many millions of farmers in the world do follow, in some fashion, the organic-farming tenets. The vast numbers who till the soil in India and China, for instance, use almost no chemical pesticides or fertilizers. Such organic matter as they return, even including human excrement, is totally insufficient.

The incidence of malnutrition and starvation in those areas is well enough known to make further comment needless, other than to add that it would be unfair to attribute all the agricultural inadequacies of those oriental farmers to this or to any single cause. The relentless pests which unceasingly threaten the world's food supply utilize all the abundant weapons with which nature has equipped them. If man is to keep ahead of the bugs and ahead of depleted soils in his battle against hunger—a contest that will become more rather than less difficult—he will rely increasingly upon the proven products of the agricultural chemical industries.

PART THREE:

As of Today and Tomorrow

18/Biological Controls

SCIENTISTS HAVE FOUND A FEW IDEAL METHODS FOR COM-
batting the insect pest. They set enemies against him, or
make him sick, or prevent him from reproducing. These procedures and others that require no chemical assistance are
called biological controls. Unhappily, they are not always applicable, and do not always work.

Those most noxious insect pests that emigrated here from
other countries may not have been serious nuisances in their
home lands. Their original surroundings perhaps did not
provide the contiguous acres of foods that have stimulated
their multiplication here. Their numbers at home may have
been restrained by native parasites or predators, which the
immigrant left behind when it came to this land of liberty.

Consequently, when an alien insect becomes a high-
powered troublemaker, our entomologists scour its indigenous territory to search for its natural enemies. If they find a
prospect, they have to make sure that it will not also become
a pest here. If satisfied on that point, they introduce it with
the hope that it may reduce or annihilate the pest. The old
line, "Let's you and him fight," expresses the idea.

Failures and partial successes have resulted. But the first and still best known application succeeded brilliantly.

A tiny insect called the cottony-cushion scale had threatened to destroy the California citrus industry. After 1872, when first noted, the scale had spread widely. Not only was all the fruit lost in many groves but sometimes even the trees were being killed. Some orange and lemon growers were ready to quit, because no method of control was known.

The idea that the pest had arrived in California from Australia, and that it might have left behind a parasite, reached Charles Valentine Riley, then the USDA chief entomologist. To obtain such a parasite he had to resort to a bit of subterfuge. He was not popular with Congress. Perhaps because a member or so had objected to Riley's numerous European trips, Congress had specified that absolutely no entomology funds could be used for foreign travel. Riley discovered, however, that Congress had given the State Department an appropriation to participate in an exposition at Melbourne. He persuaded State to designate one of his top entomologists to represent the United States officially at the Melbourne show.

Albert Koebele, an able scientist who may have first suggested an Australian search, got the job. Soon after reaching Australia, Koebele, who lingered not long around the Melbourne exposition, learned that the vedalia beetle ate both eggs and larvae of the cottony-cushion scale and apparently cared for nothing else. In seven months after his arrival in September 1888, he sent several shipments, a total of 514 beetles, to California. These received good care and multiplied rapidly. Soon thousands were released in the citrus groves. They did their work so well that the destructive scale has never since been a problem. The vedalias are still kept on hand and released when occasion requires.

This was not a highly expensive endeavor, even for the State Department. The Australian search was accomplished for less than $5,000. The value to the California citrus industry was many thousands, perhaps millions, of times that amount. Among Koebele's later achievements was to discover the Australian lady beetle, a different predator, which has kept another pest, the citrophilus mealy bug, under control.

A USDA statement in *Agricultural Research,* October 1962, called this:

> . . . a striking instance—and a striking exception, time has proved—of the effectiveness of biological control of insect pests. . . . More often, biological control efforts have only helped to partially control insect pests. . . . Efforts have been made to import many of these natural enemies, but the desired balance between the pest and the beneficial insect has seldom been achieved.

Since the vedalia beetle triumph government entomologists have searched the earth, hoping to repeat that success. They have brought in some 650 species of predators and parasites. About one hundred of these have become established; none has ever matched the vedalia's performance, although about twenty have proved to be useful.

Another moderate success in biological control developed on the opposite side of the country, in New Jersey. Here it was that the first Japanese beetle is supposed to have landed in the Western world, probably as an egg or larva hidden around the roots of a nursery importation. The presence of this metallic-looking, rather handsome beetle was first observed in 1916.

The beetle discovered no shortage of foodstuffs and steadily it invaded more territory in the East. Orchard crops, small fruits, shade trees, ornamentals and flowers attracted its attention. In all it has found nourishment from some 275 different plants. The adult seems to be especially fond of roses, which it attacks in the bud and whose bloom it wholly ruins.

When the grubs are numerous underground they damage grass and turf severely. Man's involuntary support for this voracious immigrant costs, according to careful estimates, around $10,000,000 a year.

Quarantine measures soon proved to be too late and hopeless. As the seriousness of the beetle's expansion became evident, half a hundred different predators and parasites were imported from Japan, Korea, Formosa, China, India and Hawaii. Two of them, both small wasps, begin to help; they lay eggs in the beetle grub; when hatched the young consume the grub. But the beetles out-multiply the wasps.

A sharp-eyed entomologist named G.F. White, while examining the beetle situation in central New Jersey in 1933, noted that some of the grubs seemed to be whiter than others. Under a microscope he found the reason. The grubs were full of tiny spores, each so minute that a single grub when fully infected may contain two billion of them. Peculiarly the spores resist cold, heat, moisture and dryness, and survive in the ground for years. They will not grow, though, in any other medium than in grubs.

Another entomologist, who was also a bacteriologist, S.R. Dutky, evolved a process to help the spores to get around. Grubs are inoculated, and when filled with the disease spores they are ground up, and additives provided to make a dust. Rather expensive to prepare in this way but effective, when applied to areas where the beetle grubs are numerous the spores go promptly to work.

The infection in the grubs is called, from their appearance, milky disease. The spore dust has now been distributed widely enough that heavy beetle infestations are largely a thing of the past where the insect was once most destructive.

Yet neither the wasps nor the milky disease have by any means obliterated the Japanese beetle. In recent years insecticides have been added to the opposition arsenal, some of them with fair effectiveness. The beetle travels gladly by air or by any other means of transport, and has been found likely to show up almost anywhere east of the Mississippi and two-thirds of the way southward toward the Gulf. Your author lives within five miles of the place where the Japanese intruder was first found and closer yet to the laboratory where most of the control measures were worked out. Last summer's roses entertained a few beetles.

In common with humankind, insects maintain an active interest in sex. Their extraordinary reproduction rate leaves no doubt about that. Perhaps the fact that few of the adults need to bear responsibility for their numerous offspring, other than to see that the young emerge within reach of food, is a factor. Sex attractants have been developed to lure certain kinds of insects to their death, a story that will be told later.

What happened to the screwworm fly affords a dramatic story of how a scientist doomed an insect by taking advantage of its sexual characteristics.

The screwworm fly is a nasty creature with revolting habits. The fly itself, two or three times the size of a housefly, is marked with three streaks down its back. The female is the deadly member of the species. She lays her eggs, two or three hundred at a time, in any open wound she can find on a warm-blooded animal. A cut, a scratch, even a tick bite will serve her purpose. The navel of a new-born calf or fawn is a susceptible spot. In twelve hours the eggs will hatch and in four or five days the wound will become a pocket of maggots, each boring deeper into the helpless animal. Cattle, sheep, hogs, and goats suffer from the screwworm, as do deer and other forms of wildlife. As the wound grows in size the females will return to deposit more eggs. The maggots drop to the ground where they mature and in about two weeks emerge as flies, ready to seek more prey.

The insect had long been known in Texas, but was first found in the Southeast early in the 1930's. So rapidly did it spread that in 1934 more than 200,000 animals were reported killed in the Gulf States, and more than 1,350,000 attacked. Livestock growers had to watch their animals carefully to detect and treat infestations before animals were killed. For larger cattle owners this meant hiring more cowboys; for smaller owners, it meant less time for other operations. The annual losses for years in terms of dead and weakened animals and in extra labor costs were estimated to run up to $20,000,000 or more.

A USDA research team, following the procedure outlined by the man who conceived the idea, Dr. Edward F. Knipling, set themselves to the job of reproducing large numbers of the flies in confinement, sterilizing them with cobalt rays, and then releasing them. The point of the story is this: The adult female mates only once; so if it mates with a male that is sterile, no offspring result.

A preliminary test on the island of Curaçao eradicated the pest from that small area. Knipling and his associates then set up a screwworm "factory" in an airplane hangar at Sebring, Florida, in which to raise the screwworm flies. With the aid of forty tons of ground whale and horse meat they were able to produce fifty to seventy million flies a week. At a definite stage the pupae were subjected to the sterilizing cobalt rays.

Surveys in various areas of Florida, Georgia and Alabama indicated the numbers of wild screwworm flies at large. From airplanes the sterile flies were dropped over the entire area in boxes about the size of frozen food packages. The idea was to turn out about ten to twenty-five sterile males for every female believed to be at large. The planes flew in repeated, systematic patterns for more than three million miles.

Within eighteen months the vicious insect was totally eradicated from the Southeast. The operation cost about

$10,000,000—no more than half the losses the screwworms had inflicted in one of their mildest years.

The same method has been reducing the Texas screwworm infestation. There the insects' presence in nearby Mexico complicates the problem. With the Mexican government's cooperation planes have been dropping sterile males below the border in a zone up to 200 miles over which the females will not fly except in very low numbers. Total eradication of the pest from U.S. territory is expected.

Thus, by three methods of biological control, a predator, a disease, and male sterilization, three species of destructive insects have been greatly reduced or exterminated. But ten thousand species are considered to be injurious to man's interests in the United States, and of these at least a hundred are extremely serious pests.

Dr. Knipling's idea achieved a second experimental success on the distant Pacific island of Rota. The melon fly, a pernicious pest, attacks a variety of vegetable crops. By releasing sterile males the melon fly was eradicated from the island.

A related experiment on the same island eliminated another destructive pest, the oriental fruit fly. In this instance the biological method was combined with use of a chemical insecticide. It had been learned that methyl eugenol is a potent attractant to the oriental fruit fly male. By combining the attractant with an insecticide called maled, the species was exterminated from the island.

The quest for ways to deal with insect and plant pests has a far distance yet to travel. The sciences that apply to agriculture are mostly less than a century old. Economic entomology and plant pathology are among their juniors. So it is not strange that relatively little is yet known about many of the mysterious processes within the lives of insects and plants. Recognizing this, the USDA has lately completed a new Metabolism and Radiation Research Laboratory at Fargo, North Dakota. Studies there will concentrate on finding more of the inner secrets, not only of bugs and plants but of animals, with the expectation that new knowledge will open the way to more effective use of pesticides or to better means to accomplish profitable results. Another new laboratory, at Columbia, Missouri, will be devoted to study of insect control by biological methods, utilizing insect predators, parasites, and diseases.

A long-range approach to minimizing insect damage deals with the plant instead of with the bug. Entomologists, with the necessary help of plant breeders, have undertaken to breed strains of crop plants which insects seem reluctant to attack. Varieties of wheat have been developed that are pronounced "virtually immune" to the Hessian fly. The spotted alfalfa aphid and a nematode that injures alfalfa have found distasteful the new varieties of that important forage legume that scientists have bred with that intent. A small number of other successes at producing resistant plant varieties have been had. The plant breeder has to try not only for resistance but to maintain yield and other essential characteristics. The process is slow and expensive, but once a truly resistant strain has been created the only fear need be that the bugs themselves may breed strains resistant to the plant's resistance. Houseflies, it will be remembered, developed strains immune to DDT.

The fact that a half-dozen resistant varieties of crop plants have been developed, each resistant to one or more species of insect enemy, encourages effort on this front. However, when one bears in mind that most crops suffer from a few to several hundreds of insect species, and that some 250 crops are commercially important, the necessity for more immediate and more versatile weapons becomes apparent.

Farmers follow many practices which they have found will help to reduce the damage by hostile insects. The Hessian fly may be frustrated if the winter-wheat grower delays his seeding until after the fall flight of the fly has taken place. Because the date of this event fluctuates with the weather and other factors, some of them quite local, farmers usually watch for the advice of their state experiment stations to learn the safe time. By sowing accordingly, the wheat does not sprout and grow until after the flies have come and gone. When wheat is planted early it becomes infected and carries the so-called "flax seed" or resting stage over the winter to produce a new generation in the spring. The larvae cause severe damage in two ways. The heads fail to fill properly with grain; and the straw usually breaks down before the harvest time.

The European corn borer can be reduced in numbers when farmers plow under or destroy the corn stalks after harvest. If the stalks are well buried by plowing, or shredded into small pieces to be used for fodder or livestock bedding, large numbers of the larvae will be killed. Unfortunately they do not confine their interest to corn; many may survive in weeds and other plants that escape destruction.

When the cotton boll weevil's terrific assault upon that crop reached devastating proportions, the growers had no knowledge of what to do. Farm scientists advised them to destroy all stalks, rotate the crop to different fields, plant early-maturing varieties and apply enough fertilizer to hurry up the growth. These good farming methods made it possible for profitable cotton to be grown in spite of the weevil. The pink bollworm, another destructive pest which has appeared in the Southwest, is restrained by similar methods.

These farm practices constitute forms of biological control, based upon knowledge of insect habits. They lessen the damage but they do not eliminate the problems.

When biological control works completely, as it did when the vedalia beetle stopped the cottony-cushion scale in the California citrus groves, and when male sterilization wiped out the screwworm from the southeastern states, it has definite advantages. In those instances the first cost was the last; expensive annual or more frequent measures ceased to be necessary. No undesirable side effects resulted.

Unhappily, such triumphs have been rare indeed. No doubt there will be more. The tasks are immense. Even if all pest species were susceptible to the male sterilization method, which is still uncertain, the task of rearing, treating, and distributing sterilized males over the vast areas which some species infest would be huge indeed, and for most insects would be impractical.

Nevertheless research will almost certainly disclose new aspects of natural control, and new ways to combine biological, chemical or other techniques. Various entomologists, insect pathologists, and chemists associated with insect control, whose achievements command attention to their thoughts, have suggested some enticing possibilities, which are being examined. For instance, find an attractant—it might be sexual, food or chemical—that the boll weevil or some other important pest could not resist. Combine with it a fatal poison. Or put into it a disease, a virus, bacteria or what not, that would sicken not only one boll weevil but would sweep through the entire population of weevils! Give him a sort of boll-weevil smallpox, yellow fever, plague, or blight! Or even combine an attractant with a chemical sterilant.

These ideas are more than fancies and dreams. Behind them already stand enough experiments to justify the explorations that federal and state researchers now are conducting. One disease organism, *Bacillus thuringiensis,* now sold commercially, has found some, though rather limited, use to control certain crop insects. Certain viruses that affect only a given insect species are under investigation; they promise possible control for some of the insect pests.

Although widely acclaimed as a brilliantly successful proponent and demonstrator of biological approaches, Dr. Knipling has said:

It is generally recognized, however, that biological control agents cannot be used under some circumstances. Alone they are seldom effective and reliable enough to provide the degree of pest control required for modern production efficiency.

Further, the standards of quality in our farm produce that the public deserves and expects can rarely be met by the natural control agents.

19/Wildlife and Pesticides

AWARENESS TO THE RIGHTS AND DELIGHTS OF WILDLIFE IN the United States has taken a long time to develop. The bison, the most magnificent of our beasts, was almost exterminated before steps were taken to preserve a few small herds. Driven early from the East, he was pushed from the plains by relentless rifle slaughter to make room for the white man's farms and ranches. I "knew personally" the one surviving passenger pigeon before it died in the Cincinnati zoo a half century ago, hardly forty years after its species had flocked and flown in numbers incredible. The gorgeous, big ivory-billed woodpecker, once monarch of the great cypress swamps, has not been seen for a decade or more.

The plume hunters—tempted by the price milady paid for adorning her millinery—almost extinguished the beautiful American and snowy egrets. The lumbermen deprived the ivory-bill of its habitat, and no doubt the target shooter took his toll. Only a generation ago, men and boys with guns asked, "Is it good to eat?" If so, that was reason enough to shoot. Or, they said, "If it isn't good to eat, it's no good," and shot anyway. The "sportsmen" with airplanes and high-powered rifles will finish off the arctic's polar bears soon if not prevented, and even now are massacring the golden eagle. And who but gunners have brought the rare whooping crane down to a mere three dozen or thereabouts in numbers?

But let's not all of us be too smug about the brave hunter who defends himself from the onslaughts of the aggressive rabbit, the feral quail, the violent turtledove and the vicious deer! We who are too civilized and refined do not shoot the cardinals, the towhees and meadowlarks. We just want to take over their fields and woods as places to build houses. We want wider and faster highways to drive over. We want airports. We want acres of golf courses and well-mown park spaces. More than seventeen thousand migrating birds dashed themselves to death against one television tower over a six-year period, and there are more than five hundred television towers. But we want television.

We also want green trees and fruitful orchards, and want our markets to be loaded daily with perfect fruits and bug-free vegetables, plenty of bread and butter and meat.

Now we find the creatures that fly and run and swim are confronted by another hazard. Long before *Silent Spring* the pesticide makers knew that some of their products could injure wildlife, and were trying to guard against such effects. They could not always prevent misuses, especially when governmental bodies chose to apply their products to wide areas. Yet they sought to meet the public needs for products that could insure better foods and that would enable trees to survive. That all were fully alert to the dangers to wildlife I shall not assert, for I have not known them all; but now, they certainly are.

The food-chain consequences from poisonous insecticides at first were imperfectly considered. The Clear Lake affair in California has become widely known. Here, before action was taken to control an annoying gnat that was intolerably numerous, the problem was studied, because no one wanted the fish to be affected. DDD, a relative of DDT, was applied in highly diluted proportions. The gnat problem was reduced, but the attractive and interesting western grebes succumbed. Studies indicated that what the grebes ate had built up a DDD content that was fatal to them. Those who made the preparatory studies could not at that time have anticipated and certainly did not want the unhappy consequence.

Probably no single incident involving pesticides has been more widely publicized than the death of robins on the Michigan State University campus. This handsome campus is adorned by some 2,200 elms, among them many of respectable age and large size. When the bark beetles brought the deadly Dutch elm fungus to the area, the university authorities naturally moved to try to preserve their trees. State and city officials also acted in the adjacent and nearby streets and parks of East Lansing and Lansing.

Although some spraying began earlier, from 1957 the trees have been treated once each year. Until 1964, DDT was used. Not only was it used, it was applied liberally. Some of the larger trees received from two to three gallons of 25 per cent DDT emulsion at each application. Being a persistent compound, DDT in such quantities accumulated in the soil from year to year. Earthworms ingest the DDT along with their diet of soil and decaying leaves. Robins feed heavily upon earthworms and consequently, they, too, have stored lethal quantities. In one study 69 robins were analyzed for DDT in the brain; 62 were reported to have as much or more than the amount that in experimental feedings had produced death.

Some robins come to the campus each year, but most of them die without establishing a nest. Of those that do nest, few if any manage to raise a brood. "While we can't say that we have examined every bush on the campus, we have not located a successful robin nest in five years," Dr. Peter I. Tack, chairman of the university's Department of Fisheries and Wildlife, has reported. Several other bird species have not been seen or have become scarce. The data on several robin and songbird kills have been questioned by some scientists, so that the situation here and in similar cases remains controversial.

In 1964 the authorities substituted methoxychlor, a much less persistent (though more expensive) insecticide, in the elm tree sprays, probably in deference to continuous criticism.

One further fact belongs in the story: not all the elm trees have been saved. The tree losses, however, have not been extensive, probably no more than 2 per cent according to one campus observer.

What should have been done, or not done? Quite likely most pesticide specialists, even those who hesitate to concede to any doubter, would agree that the DDT quantities applied on the Michigan State University campus were excessive; they might also criticize the methods of application. The matter of quantity perhaps is crucial. Thousands of spray programs elsewhere have not produced bird kills of any such degree, or none at all. When the spraying began, perhaps the state of knowledge then indicated that the heavier dosages used were necessary to the purpose.

Here, again, rises the fact that in all sorts of human affairs the elements of risk and choice seldom absent themselves. Which adds more to the delight and charm of a college campus—elm trees or robins? One would hate to choose. A campus needs both, and the ideal would be to control the elm ailments without assassinating the birds or squirrels.

And now, happily, that can be done. The chemist's ceaseless search for better pesticides has accomplished just this purpose. A product that will kill the beetles which spread the Dutch elm fungus and will prevent infection of the healthy trees has lately been approved for that purpose. Developed by Shell Agricultural Chemical Company, its name is Bidrin. A systemic insecticide, Bidrin was first applied to cotton. To protect the elm, Bidrin is forced into the sap by pressure through a tube. It kills the beetles. The cost compares favorably with that of spraying.

Another question of choice is latent here, too. Without trees, how about the birds? The robins, cardinals, and song sparrows could make out with shrubs and bushes. But the Baltimore orioles like to weave their nesting pouches among the end twigs of a high-swinging elm branch. Most warblers and vireos nest high, and find their sustenance in the treetops. Even the jays and grackles place their nests well up in the trees. No tall trees, no orioles.

A hundred or so miles northward from the Michigan State campus an exceedingly rare species of bird nests each year and happily raises enough young to carry on. The Kirtland warbler breeds only in this one region, a few thousand acres of jack pine. Were some beetle to attack those particular trees or infest them with a fatal fungus or virus, how should that dilemma be solved? If the trees were not saved the Kirtland warbler would no doubt join the dodo and the passenger pigeon in the realms of extinction. If spraying the trees killed the birds, or the food they find. . . .

"I hope," says Dr. Stack, "that we never have to make a decision on that one, unless we know how to save them both."

Another extensively reported incident has been the discovery of large numbers of dead fish during recent winters in the waters of the Mississippi below New Orleans.

The kill affected several million menhaden, an abundant salt water species, which are seined from the sea in large numbers to make fertilizer. Fresh water species, including food varieties, also succumbed.

As this is written the true cause remains in doubt, despite rather extensive investigations by several agencies. Fish, shellfish, and crustaceans are readily susceptible to some types of insecticides, so that initial conclusions pointed to some such cause. Did residues from dusts and sprays applied to crops wash into the streams and begin their lethal work below New Orleans? An endrin plant in Memphis was suspected. Did wastes from this plant roll 751 miles downstream from Memphis to New Orleans before beginning to poison fish? Very few dead specimens were found between the two cities. Could pollutions from higher up in the Mississippi and Missouri Valleys have acquired deadly effect only after they had reached so near to the big river's mouth?

Extensive fish kills have not been rare. The so-called Red Tide at different times has been fatal to large numbers of fish off the Gulf Coast of Florida, and is known along western Africa. The specific bacterial organism identified with this danger was not present in the lower Mississippi. The possibility that some other bacterial or viral infection might have occurred has been advanced and explored.

Pesticides have neither been exonerated nor convicted of guilt in the lower reaches of Old Man River. The situation merely emphasizes the urgency that the real facts, uncolored by guesswork or prejudices, shall be brought to light.

After the publicized incidents in which wildlife seems to have been adversely affected, and where pesticides have been charged rightly or wrongly with the responsibility, considerable interest attaches to the experiences reported by an enthusiastic conservationist, fisherman, hunter and outdoor writer who for nineteen years as an agricultural pilot has been spreading insecticides over 150,000 acres or more each season. He is a Mississippian, Mabry Anderson, who appeared before a 1964 USDA hearing on pesticides in Memphis. He referred specifically to three plantations. Of one, he said:

> This is a five-thousand-acre tract lying wholly behind the Mississippi River levee, comprising roughly 3,500 acres of timber land and 1,500 acres of open or farm land. It also has five major bodies of water that are

excellent fishing lakes, these being old river runs and
so-called "blue holes." . . . Virtually all the open land
is utilized for cotton. This cotton is planted in open
fields scattered throughout the woods and some fields
are directly bounded by lakes. This cotton has always
been heavily poisoned, usually by airplane and by my
firm. For the past two years seasonal applications have
run about twelve or fourteen applications . . . for the
most part endrin and methyl-parathion. Pilots have
been instructed to report to me on sightings of deer and
wild turkey in fields being sprayed. In numerous instances they have reported that fields contained deer
and wild turkey while spraying operations were in
progress. I have personally observed all species of game
utilizing these fields daily during the entire poisoning
season. Never in any instance has there been found any
dead or sick game on this property. This property is
controlled by a private hunting club and is a model of
game and fish productivity. Deer, wild turkey, quail,
rabbits, squirrel and fur bearers are abundant and have
increased steadily for the past ten years. Deer have
become so abundant as to be a nuisance to farming
and the turkey population is estimated by the Game
and Fish Commission biologists to be as dense as any
population in the United States. Quail are abundant
in the open-type land and hunter success is higher than
average on all species of game. Although spraying operations are carried on right down to the water's edge in
lakes, no fish kills have ever been observed and fishing
is extremely good.

Anderson referred to the owner of a second plantation as
"having been a heavy poisoner back as far as the 1920's."
"During recent years," he said, "all cotton lands have been
sprayed at least twelve to fifteen times per season. This particular place is my own favorite quail hunting ground and I
have never observed any quail killed due to insecticides.
Quail populations during the past five years have been excellent."

Referring then to two other plantations, Anderson said:

These lands lie adjacent to Swan Lake, a large, relatively shallow body of water famous for duck shooting and excellent fishing. Cotton land lies completely around this lake and continuous seasonal insect control programs are in effect, the majority of it being done by airplane. All common insecticides are used, with endrin, DDT, and methyl-parathion predominating. No duck die-off has ever been observed in the lake. . . . There can be no question whatever that this lake receives a continuous run-off from all cotton lands around it, and yet no harmful effects can be observed on game and fish in the area.

While describing his operations, Anderson said:

My field men, particularly the flag boys who mark for spraying airplanes in the field, have been instructed to watch carefully for any wildlife found dead or dying. On only one occasion, in 1950 or 1951, two rabbits were found dead in a field that had been sprayed with tetra-ethylpyrophosphate, applied in an effort to control red spider mites. On one other occasion, about ten years ago, toxaphene dust was seen to drift into a small bayou-type lake and a minor fish kill was observed a few days later. It might be interesting to note that sport fishing improved considerably shortly thereafter, the greatest problem with fishing in the Delta being overpopulation.

Concluding his testimony, Anderson said:

As a result of almost twenty years of such observation, I am strongly inclined to classify the furore raised regarding insecticide use as a "witch hunt." It is completely inconceivable to me that the waters of the lower Mississippi River can be contaminated by insecticides when the waters lying adjacent to cotton fields are not contaminated. It must be admitted that minor fish kills are occasionally reported but from a practical standpoint they are nothing. Fish kills are often carried out by authorities for the purpose of improving fishing. The Mississippi Delta as a whole absorbs the heaviest concentration of economic poisons in the entire country, and yet it is an admitted fact that the game and fish populations are higher in the Delta than almost anywhere else in the United States. . . . Game and Fish Commission data in the states of Mississippi, Arkansas and Louisiana will prove this conclusively. To become overly concerned with a few minor, and often unproved, claims of wildlife damage is ridiculous. . . . Naturally, all necessary precautions should be adhered to in applying any toxic material, but the overall benefits received greatly outweigh the slight risk involved in their use.

All birds watchers know the name of Roger Tory Peterson. He is author and artist of the most widely used bird identification guides and eminent also as an ornithological scientist. Dr. Peterson recommends that all chlorinated hydrocarbon insecticides should be withdrawn from use. He expresses special concern "about those species that are at the end of long food-chains, particularly fish-eating birds." He refers to diminishing numbers of ospreys, which usually live and nest around estuarine waters, to eagles, hawks, and pelicans in coastal areas. Dr. Peterson has also remarked upon the "several species that are enjoying a boom—redwing blackbirds, starlings and grackles—birds that are not so subject to poisons in their food because they are mainly granivorous rather than insectivorous." He discounts the argument that the annual Christmas bird counts show increasing numbers of birds because each year more people participate and count more efficiently: "A count of two million birds in a southern state is likely to mean nearly two million blackbirds."

The graceful and rapacious gulls, especially the big herring gulls, which combine the characteristics of buzzards and hawks, constantly scavenge the river mouths and sea shores. A dead fish seldom escapes their prompt attention. These birds have apparently been increasing each year in numbers, and no die-off has been observed. Nor are the carrion-feeding end-of-chain turkeys and black buzzards disappearing.

The reference to the starlings and blackbirds brings up another point. Since the first few pairs were imported from Europe some seventy-five years ago, starlings have spread over nearly all sections of the nation. Aggressive and voracious, they fight with bluebirds and purple martins and woodpeckers for nesting sites. Their habit of congregating in thousands around city buildings to roost in winter has not improved their popularity. Omnivorous eaters, they impartially consume insects and food crops. The redwing blackbird, in the East at least, seems to have taken over most of the meadows and hayfields where once the bobolink, meadowlark, and vesper sparrow made their homes. Redwings and grackles have become serious late summer pests in sweet corn and other grain fields. No avicide specific for the overwhelming starling has been marketed; although one new oral toxicant is said to show promise for use in selected places, such as northern cattle-feeding lots, where starlings gather in large numbers in winter while other birds are absent. Starling roosts have been blamed for epidemics of a lung disease, histoplasmosis, at Mason City, Iowa, and Dexter, Missouri. The disease develops from a fungus which spreads in the birds' droppings.

In search of further light on the wild-bird insecticide dispute let us turn to *Miscellaneous Bulletin* No. 4404, issued in 1961 by the Pennsylvania Department of Agriculture. It was written by James O. Nichols, entomologist, Pennsylvania Department of Agriculture, and State Forest Entomologist, Pennsylvania Department of Forests and Waters.

From 1944 to 1958 DDT was sprayed by airplane over 1,107,458 acres to destroy the gypsy moth larvae, which were denuding trees. The dosage was one pound per acre. No gypsy moths survived. The following paragraphs are quoted from *Bulletin* 1044:

Observations from numerous, carefully controlled experiments conducted by the United States Fish and Wildlife Service and other agencies have been made to determine the effects on wildlife. As a result of these tests, the Fish and Wildlife Service has publicly stated that up to two pounds of DDT per acre does not have an appreciable effect on birds, earthworms, mammals, or reptiles, including reproduction of species. The view is substantiated by observations of the Pennsylvania Department of Agriculture and the Pennsylvania Game Commission.

Concern has been shown by wildlife enthusiasts for the effects DDT would have on birds. However, experiments conclusively show that birds have a considerable tolerance for DDT. A few such examples will point this out.

Several tests were conducted in Pennsylvania during the years 1944 to 1958 by the United States Department of Agriculture, Fish and Wildlife Service and Pennsylvania Department of Agriculture biologists and entomologists. This included a 52,000 acre forest tract. Careful censuses were taken by ornithologists of bird life prior to, during, and following the spraying. In initial experiments five pounds of DDT in five gallons of oil solution were applied per acre. This resulted in minor mortality to birds and most insectivorous species left the area for several weeks. The dosage was then reduced to one and two pounds per acre. No mortality was noted at these dosages and evidence of modified behavior was minor. This modified behavior occurred mainly in marsh and aquatic areas where a few species of birds—swallows, flycatchers, and others of similar feeding habits—temporarily abandoned sprayed areas for about a week. There was no evidence that the temporary reduction of insects by spraying at one pound per acre was of any real consequence to birds. Development and survival of nestling young was normal at this dosage.

A great deal of interest was aroused in these experiments, particularly with the Scranton, Pennsylvania, Bird Club and the National Audubon Society, as to the effect DDT would have on songbirds. The membership of the Scranton Bird Club, about four hundred, kept a close check on these operations. Despite their vigilance, not a single case of poisoning attributable to the DDT treatment at one pound per acre was reported. Officials of the National Audubon Society were satisfied that no damage was done to bird life, including nestling birds.

Among the bulletin's summary paragraphs, Nichols says:

> The gypsy moth is an extremely destructive insect to shade trees and hardwood forests, especially those predominantly oak. . . . Defoliation for two or three consecutive years is sufficient to either directly kill trees affected or to so weaken them that they are easy targets for secondary insects and diseases. Coniferous trees may be killed by one complete defoliation. . . .
> Rather than disrupt the "balance of nature," treatments to eradicate the gypsy moth have preserved and improved the forest lands to the benefit of every form of life. Spraying operations have restored these lands to their former condition, complete with wildlife which previously existed before the moth decimated the tree cover and made an inhospitable environment.

Little has been said about the present and potential benefits pesticides may provide for wildlife, such as Nichols mentions have resulted from gypsy moth control. The Great Lakes offer one instance. There the whitefish and lake trout were en route to extermination by the lamprey eel, which attached itself to them and fed to their death. A specific chemical now is gradually eradicating the eel. The commercial fishing for trout and whitefish, long a considerable industry, is expected to be restored.

Elimination of the screwworm from the Southeast relieved deer and other wild as well as the domestic animals from the painful and often fatal wounds that pest inflicted.

Materials for removing strangling plant growth from streams and lakes to make them more habitable for fish, and for eliminating overpopulations of trash fish, have been in profitable use for several years.

Not much is known about the diseases that affect birds in the wild. Encephalitis is transmitted by mosquitoes to birds and from birds to humans. Since other fauna and flora are affected by numerous diseases, it is reasonable to suppose that the animals and birds of which we are particularly fond have their own untreated medical problems. All wild birds seem to have lice, mites or both. One might guess that insecticidal reduction of mosquitoes, mites, and other known disease vectors has benefitted some of the birds. To what degree the avian population is infested with nematodes, or life-shortening bacteria and viruses, remains a field to be more fully explored.

If all these facts and opinions tend to leave one a bit uncertain, that would seem to be about the current status.

We have the one inescapable and implacable condition: more millions of people to demand living space and healthful food. To find the living and working space, wildlife has been pushed aside since the first decades of the continent's settlement. Pesticides have added a new element of hazard, at a time when many more of us than ever before are appreciative of wildlife values.

Compared to the enormous benefits to man in terms of life, health, food and costs, the wildlife tragedies, regrettable as they are, have been only occasional, and mostly reversible, because in most instances where they have occurred the species will recover. Where man builds his houses and destroys the habitat, the wildlife must go elsewhere, or die.

Between bugs and people the choices are not difficult. Between pests and wildlife, they are not so easy. Nor are those choices yet so sure as they will become. The next few years—

soon enough, we hope, before much irreparable injury can be done—will see vastly more certainty about how fish, birds and animals are being affected. Large sums are now being devoted to studying the questions involved. Meanwhile research also is producing less hazardous means of pesticide control, both through new materials and new methods of application.

The problem is far from being ignored. Every conservation organization is alert to it. Government is providing funds to find out more about it. Industry is seeking to develop materials that will reduce and, where possible, abolish the problem.

The prospect of a silent spring is not imminent. It may be doubted sincerely that one ever will befall us.

20/Finding and Making Pesticides

NOW THAT WE HAVE BEEN TALKING FOR PAGES AND PAGES about pesticides, let us consider making one together. It seems to be a good business. At least the products obviously are highly necessary, the best ones are likely to be accepted in a big way, and we shall be conferring benefits upon our fellow man.

First, let's start with an idea. I'll furnish that. You put up the money and find the brains. We'll aim for something that is badly needed. Say, maybe, an insecticide that will kill boll weevils at any stage of their malignant lives. Or, better yet, one that will kill *all* the cotton insects. That's really dreaming up a miracle. But, DDT and 2.4-D seemed like miracles, too.

Still, those ideas are fairly obvious. Someone surely is working on them, and may be far ahead of us. So, as long as our target at this point is merely theoretical, let's shoot for the moon. How about trying for a systemic insecticide that could be mixed into seeds before planting, or washed on the roots of things like cabbage and tomatoes before the plants are set out, and that without any undesirable effects would

render any crop resistant or even lethal to all its insect enemies.

That's surely a wild one, but think of the potential sales!
Even now, like as not, in the secrecy of private laboratories
some crew of crazy scientists may be groping toward some
such amazing product. But we can dream, and when we get
down to work we shall decide what we can produce.

So, how do we start? First of all, we'll need to assemble a
staff.

One of our competitors employs thirty Ph.D.'s, and twenty-
five persons with masters' and bachelors' degrees. Another
reports having forty-four Ph.D.'s, fourteen M.S.'s and eighty-
one B.S.'s working on new products. So we'll have to find and
hire a similar staff, with much the same variety of special
disciplines.

These people will need the best of laboratory facilities.
Such facilities are bound to run into seven big figures, count-
ing all the land, buildings, and highly refined equipment.
The people we hope to employ are a breed of scientific ideal-
ists; when they search for new knowledge they go where they
can find the best tools. We can't scrimp. A mere laboratory
by itself will not be enough. We must also have greenhouses,
maybe eight, a dozen, or more of them, and five or six buildings in which to house our test animals. And we could not
expect to expose our product, assuming that we find a prom-
ising prospect, until after doing our own field testing. For
that we must have a fair-sized farm, say a section of 640 acres,
or maybe more. Possibly one farm will not be enough. We
know competitors who operate test farms in the North, West
and South.

Shall we start now? It would have helped decidedly if we
had already had a few decades of experience in this sort of
business. Suppose we have had. Also suppose that you know
where the money will come from to keep on going, once we
do get rolling. May take quite a bit.

Was anything said about a library? We would be foolish to repeat experiments someone else has already done and reported. Yet, some such abandoned experiment might start one of our Ph.D.'s off on a valuable new trail. So there must be shelves of books and papers and a well-trained scientific library staff. We must provide subscriptions to all appropriate scientific and trade magazines. If our library doesn't have everything we need, access to university and government libraries will help the preliminary search of all available literature touching upon the trails we propose to pursue.

The library research is crucial. After all, we are seeking a certain unknown or unrecognized combination of molecules that will accomplish a very specific work. Since molecules could be combined in several billion different ways, our staff can't be asked to start working in so vast a darkness as that. They will report that a million and a half or more compounds already have been prepared, and that their first leads will probably come from among such existing combinations or, more likely, from something suggested by the way certain of these are known to behave.

"A chemical compound," our director of research will explain to us, "is not a mere mixture of chemical substances. It is itself a distinctive substance, with its own identity, created as other chemical materials have been, that is, a number of different atoms combined in definitely fixed proportions."

The literature has been searched. The staff has put together a list of compounds to be screened, or that they will attempt to compose, using their backgrounds of personal knowledge, suggestions derived from the literature, and maybe a few pure hunches. Before they go to the laboratory they may eliminate a few. This one is restricted by patents; raw material for that one will be rare and too expensive. As they proceed they may prepare others. But a few preliminary prospects remain—four, five, maybe even ten thousand of them.

At this point we can take advantage of a pesticide maker's actual experience. When the Senate subcommittee was investigating pesticides in 1963, a witness appeared bearing a chart that was folded up accordion fashion. Each newspaper-sized page described a step in finding, making, and preparing to market a pesticide. When the accordion was fully unfolded it stretched out for sixty feet. The tall, well-built witness with a pleasant voice and gracious, Scandinavian sort of presence, was Dr. Julius E. Johnson, manager of the Bioproducts Department of the Dow Chemical Company. His presentation excited admiration, not only from the committee but from men in competing companies.

Dr. Johnson told the committee that, as a ten-year average, his group had examined 4,150 compounds each year. "The objective," he said, "is the discovery of potentially useful activity."

When we ponder that remark we immediately revise our original intention to hunt only for a boll weevil killer. Why screen thousands of compounds and ignore any one of them that may possibly be useful? After all, the needs are many.

This means that we must keep on hand a representative variety of living insects and plants with fair numbers of each. We must be able to test our compounds also for effects on fungi, bacteria, nematodes, rodents, weeds and whatever else the search may suggest. Also, as we look for chemical values we check compounds on algae, daphnia, fish, and snails to learn the effects on food-chain and aquatic organisms. Niagara Chemical reports that its "zoo" requires each year more than 10 million agricultural insects, 500,000 flies and 100,000 roaches for biological screening purposes.

While going to all this trouble we may as well also keep an eye out for effects other than killing power. Maybe the keen eyes of our initial experimenters will discover something that will stimulate or modify growth; or something that will attract or repel insects, or inhibit the capacity of an insect or animal to reproduce.

As Dr. Johnson led the way through the first stage of finding a salable pesticide, we noted the men with the test tubes,
putting new compounds together and considering old ones.
We saw them applying various dosages to insects, plants and
other test objects. About those preliminary screening processes we could see nothing but hard work. Just brute force
and manly patience, trying this combination and that, on this
bug, weed, rat, or fish, trying and watching, day after day.

Other things are involved, too, in this first stage, which
stretches out anywhere from one to two years. The scientists
compare what they are working on with whatever they know
is competitive; they synthesize related compounds. They explore the toxicity to humans, to wildlife, to benign insects,
and look into every respect where poisonousness may be a
factor. Every single observation is written down. Facts are
put through high-speed data-processing equipment. Here's
something no one expected, and here are outcomes we predicted.

Chief, here are the results! We have done all and everything we could think of with these more than four thousand
compounds.

And here are three that, for one reason or another, may be
worth experimenting with further. Only three out of four
thousand! Well, that's par for the course. (Over a ten-year
period Dow produced and marketed twenty-seven compounds out of some 41,000 screened.)

Now the one to two years of patient, arduous early laboratory work have been completed. Tedious job, one would say.
But the exciting result is that now we have two or three
candidates for further and more intense study. The second
stage will not take so long; perhaps only six months.

First we look back over what we have done so far to check
the apparent performance against whatever standards previous experiences provide. Before using up more time we had
better review the patent situation, to make sure that if one or

more of the three candidates may survive we shall not find ourselves unable to market a product. Next we have to make sure that we fully understand the structure of the compounds, and can be certain of their purity.

Those things done, what are the potential markets? What will the product cost the consumer? What sort of return may he expect if he buys it? And what may we expect if we finally decide to manufacture it? Unless it will pay at all points, we can't afford to spend more money on it.

What about its safety? That must always be a primary consideration. So we proceed to complete "acute toxicology tests," to discover if there are obviously undesirable characteristics. For three to four months we will be putting rubber tubes down the gullets of rats, rabbits, guinea pigs, and chickens, trying doses at perhaps a half-dozen levels on four or five of each. The doses may be undiluted or mixed with water or corn oil. Each animal will be observed for fourteen days. By then we will have a preliminary idea of the compound's oral toxicity.

How actively do these three candidates perform? What are their limitations? We need to know before spending more time and money. In laboratories, greenhouses, growth chambers and at field stations we look to see how each prospect responds to extremes of temperature, intensity of light, to moisture, acidity and alkalinity. We note what happens in the way of leaching, and the extent to which it degrades and disappears with the weather.

We must know still more about the possible dangers. Investigations determine the effects, if any, upon the eyes and skins of laboratory animals. What about wildlife? Having learned that a Japanese species of quail, the coturnix, can be reliably reproduced and makes a dependable and manageable test bird, we make checks with them and with chickens. If the preliminary tests turn out badly with one, we toss it out and go ahead with another. Or we may have to drop them all.

What happens with water creatures? We experiment with trout, yellow perch, blue gills, lake emerald shiners, goldfish, snails, algae and daphnia.

Who are *we* by this time? Biochemists, toxicologists, pathologists, chemists, medical technicians, a veterinarian, an M.D. trained in pharmacology, some twenty in all. And where are we? Out of four thousand prospects to begin with, now only two remain that show promise of commerical success. And we are still four years away from being ready to market a product.

For the two remaining candidates we have considerable data on performance, limitations and safety, and have made some comparisons with competitive products. Now we shall need more money; probably another half-million dollars for a surviving candidate to reach the point of sale. No longer can we proceed with the two or two dozen pounds of a compound that were enough for laboratory and preliminary tests. To produce larger quantities a pilot plant has to be set up, in which also the manufacturing processes can be refined.

As soon as we have enough of the compound, we go to the company's farms. None of the pesticide at this stage goes outside the company. Whatever produce is treated on company farms, if at all likely to be contaminated with residues, will be destroyed. The varied locations permit testing under differing environments, on several crops, and by the local farm management practices. The same machines that a farmer would use are employed. Supplemental irrigation on each location helps to study the leaching and persistence. The results are figured out to find whether a farmer would find it profitable to buy the product.

At the same time the toxicity studies are refined by further tests on skin and eyes, and by inhalation. Rats and dogs, chickens and quail, are fed for two whole years to see what may happen to them. Other farm animals will undergo tests, as well as fish and aquatic species. Does the product affect reproduction? Rats and quail help to answer that.

Dr. Johnson keeps asking more questions. "Is the pesticide stable or does it degrade? If stable, does it leach in the soil or wash off in surface water? If it leaches, how fast? Where does it go and in what concentration? Does it concentrate in living organisms or does it dilute progressively in water? Is it decomposed by hydrolysis, oxidation, ultraviolet light, or by micro-organisms in the soil?"

What if a residue remains when the crop is harvested? That must be fully investigated. Is it identical with the pesticide that was applied, or has some environmental or biochemical circumstance changed its form?

All these questions about what happens to the pesticide after it has been used had better be answered in advance. Someone is sure to ask, and the less doubt the better. Dow reports that it has sixteen scientists—others may have more— who are engaged all the time in studying nothing but metabolism and residues. Amongst these doctors are biochemists, analytical chemists, and organic chemists. Part of the time they have help from physicists, radiochemists, and others. All the standard procedures are followed, plus a few newer ones, among them some that will detect amounts as low as $\frac{1}{10}$ to $\frac{1}{100}$ part per million. No doubt you are familiar with radioisotopes, infra-red spectroscopy, visible and ultraviolet light spectroscopy, electron-affinity-gas-phase chromotography, paper and column chromotography, electrophesis, polarimetry, respirometry, spectrophotofluorometry, mass spectroscopy and X-ray spectroscopy. (Don't be embarrassed; your author only hopes he has spelled some of them right.) It is hardly necessary to add that the machines for tests such as these do not come from the dime store.

Finally, after three or four years, a considerable range of important facts can be counted up. The company has data on production methods and costs of manufacture, on the product metabolism and possible residue; knows its performance and can write preliminary directions for its use; can figure what the product should be worth to its users; and knows all that can be learned about its safety to fish, wildlife, the workers in the production plant, to the pesticide applicator, and if a residue remains, about its safety to the ultimate consumer of the crops it may treat.

Hooray! Are we now ready to begin to confer the blessing of our new product upon the buying public, and to take in their dollars in return for all that we have done?

No, a big NO! Not by a jugful, and a fairly large jug, too. We know that the product is safe. We know that it is effective for its purpose. We know that we could make money selling it because we know that our customers would make money by using it.

We know that we have a new chemical tool. That it has value we have proved to ourselves. But who else knows that important fact? And who would care?

So we prepare a technical bulletin that, in scientific and precise language, tells what our product is, what we know its limitations are, and what we think its values are. With it we send samples to the state agricultural experiment stations, to the USDA Agricultural Research Service, to the Fish and Wildlife Service and to the U.S. Public Health Service. We want them to know what a good thing we have. We tell them all we know about it and how to handle it safely. And if they can find fault with it, we want to know that now rather than later. Trials may be made in as many as thirty different geographical areas.

Nor is this usually the whole story to this point. We may have employed independent, private laboratories to check some of the results we have recorded. If they can find anything we have overlooked, we want to know. Their services, like our own, are pretty expensive, but less expensive than making a mistake in putting an article of this nature on the market.

By now we have in hand not only our own extensive and exhaustive investigations, but the results from several competent and highly critical outside evaluators. They are favorable.

Start selling now?

No, not so hastily. The law's protections intervene. But we prepare a label and submit it to the U.S. Department of Agriculture. We have to satisfy them that the product will be safe for people to use, and that it will be effective for its purpose. With critical and careful study the USDA officials comb all our data. They may take several months before deciding to give their approval. They okay our label, perhaps with a change or two. The Secretary of Agriculture finally grants our registration.

If evidence anywhere along the line has indicated that a food product likely to reach the ultimate consumer may carry a trace of residue, the equally alert and cautious Food and Drug Administration must also study our compound. That will likely take more than a few months. They have been known to ask for tests on thirty crops from twenty-five states, and for ten analyses on each of some seven hundred samples. The tolerance they permit will be, as we know, about $\frac{1}{100}$ of what the most exacting of the many tests has indicated will be perfectly safe to human health.

By now we have invested a lot of time, probably anywhere from three to seven years. And a lot of money—probably $3 to $5 million.

All that remains is to train our sales force thoroughly, train the applicators and users, and then to advertise and sell.

21/The Law's Protection

ARRIVING FROM SOUTH AMERICA AT ONE OF OUR AIRPORTS, I watched the customs inspector stir around through my soiled linen. Nearby I saw another uniformed man slice in two an orange from the baggage of a fellow passenger. He tossed the halves, and the other oranges, into a container behind him. "Mediterranean fruit fly maggots," he explained.

"Saw some down there," the passenger grinned, and made no protest.

It was probably one such infested orange from an incoming suitcase that released the fruit fly over Florida in the 1956 outbreak. Eradication had cost nearly $10 million, and if not stopped the fly would have cost hundreds of millions.

On an average of every seventeen minutes during the twenty-four-hour day, a pest is intercepted somewhere at one of the ports of entry. Not so far appearing in the United States are some 25,000 kinds of insects and diseases, damaging to crops, livestock or man, that we do not want. A single day at a busy international airport in New York has seen nearly half a ton of fruits and vegetables confiscated.

Most of us make our only acquaintance with the law when

it moves in to protect our rights, persons, or property. We read about the FBI, and the Secret Service that protects presidents and ferrets out counterfeiters, and we see the state troopers on the highways and our local police. Besides the FBI and the Secret Service some other federals, unsung and seldom publicized, perform valiant if not dangerous services for all of us, and armed with considerable authority to serve.

This border and port job is done by Plant and Animal Quarantine men. Around the nation's perimeter are 545 Plant Quarantine Division inspectors alert to see that none of those 25,000 foreign enemies of man and his possessions enters the United States. Also, 120 Animal Inspection and Quarantine men watch to see that no new or old ailments enter on four feet.

During 1961–62, these inspectors headed off the dread khapra beetle 249 times, stopped the feared golden nematode eighty-three times, and on 949 occasions prevented entrance of three destructive citrus diseases not found here. They checked 40 million packages in the mails and, in cooperation with customs, looked into more than 24 million pieces of baggage. They found 385,000 lots of illegal plant materials and intercepted 36,000 lots of dangerous insects, plant diseases, nematodes, mites, and snails.

This may not be highly dramatic work, but the consequences could well be worse than dramatic if it were not done. Not only mail and baggage, but ships, planes, trains, and automobiles are inspected at border points. Even in such importations as sheet steel, barbed wire, gums, dried hides and automobiles the men have found snails, nematodes, beetles and other undesirables. They look over all incoming commercial shipments of agricultural materials and by-products.

The regular customs inspector takes first look at the baggage. When he finds anything of a plant or animal nature he calls the plant-quarantine man. The latter decides whether it may be admitted, has to be subjected to fumigation or other treatment, or must be destroyed as inadmissible. The animal and plant inspectors also, upon an exporter's request, examine outgoing shipments to see that they meet the requirements of the countries to which they are consigned. The animal men make certain that livestock being sent abroad are healthy and being humanely handled. Incoming animals of certain classes must spend periods in quarantine to determine whether they carry infections that may not be evident upon first arrival.

The Plant Quarantine Division is a part of the U.S. Department of Agriculture. A government entomologist, Dr. Charles L. Marlatt, saw early in the century that without enforceable preventive means the country could be inundated with hundreds of undesirable insects. Largely due to his efforts, Congress in 1912 authorized the Plant Quarantine Service.

Many who should know better believe that the United States Department of Agriculture was created for farmers. While USDA is concerned with agriculture, its special province, it does not function as a special agency in *behalf* of agricultural interests. As do other governmental establishments from the Presidency down, it works for the public, for everybody.

Farmers do benefit from much that USDA does. But the basic purpose is to help advance the national economy, to encourage ample production of food and fiber for all the people, and to protect the public's health, inasmuch as food and health are intimately related. As also with other governmental establishments from the White House down, USDA is manned by human beings who make occasional errors, and is subject to the tendency to proliferate that is innate in most tax-supported bodies.

After all the criticisms have been heard, no one can question that the department's achievements in research and education, and its services in the regulatory assignments, have

benefitted the nation to a degree so enormous that the costs of these can only be rated as trivial.

By preventing objectionable pests from invading the country, the Plant Quarantine Service has saved for the economy the expenses for pesticides, and the labor of making and applying them that would follow new introduction, to say nothing of the inevitable losses any new pests cause. By prevention, it has reduced the need for pesticides.

USDA also exercises the responsibility to decide what pesticides may be used and how they may be used. No pest-killing product can be marketed in interstate commerce until USDA has granted registration.

Every proposed pesticide is presumed to be "guilty" until its proponents prove that it is not. It is "arrested" before it gets going, and does not enjoy the human offender's right to be presumed innocent until proved guilty. This, of course, is as it should be; the chemical industries fully concur that this is the proper procedure.

Two major questions face the USDA when a new pesticide is brought for registration. Most important, will it be safe to use? Then, will it do what it promises to do?

The Pesticides Regulation Division employs an array of sixty-five highly equipped chemists, biologists, entomologists, pharmacologists, toxicologists, bacteriologists, and plant pathologists. All these are experienced experts with access to every sort of detailed records that concern each question they have to answer, and with authority to require any additional information they may need from the registrant.

When food is in any way involved they work with fellow scientists in the Food and Drug Administration. If a residue remains on or in food, feed, milk, or meat, FDA determines the legal tolerance. The tolerance is normally set at a level no higher than 1/100 of the amount found to show no effects on the most susceptible test animals, and is usually established below that point. This hundred to one factor assumes that

people may be ten times as sensitive as the healthy animals tested, and that aged, very young or sick humans may be ten times as sensitive as normal persons.

The USDA men consult with Public Health Service in areas of pesticide labeling where that agency may assist them. They confer with the Fish and Wildlife Service. They study the hundreds of pages that record the exhaustive tests the manufacturer has had conducted before presenting his application. If these are not adequate they ask for more data, and wait until it is provided before registering.

Typical examples were given by Dr. M.R. Clarkson, then associate administrator of the Agricultural Research Service, when he explained the procedures to the Senate special committee investigating pesticides:

> A spray might control insects on almond trees without leaving a residue on the almonds—but almond hulls are fed to cattle, which presents the possibility of illegal residues in meat or milk. No registration for this product is approved until this question is resolved.
>
> A fungicide might control mold and mildew on plasterboard, wallpaper or plywood—but leave a hazard for the construction men who handle these materials or for people who live in the houses built. No registration is issued until the question is resolved.

Comparable studies determine whether the compound will be effective for its purpose when put to use. After these questions have been determined affirmatively, a label has to be approved, a label that makes clear what the material should be used for, how it should be applied, and what precautions must be observed by users. USDA demands simple wording, and prescribes even the size of type for certain features of labeling.

Once registration has been granted, the maker has no promise that it will be permanent. Should significant new

adverse evidence appear, the Secretary of Agriculture may and sometimes does revoke the registration or require changes in the labels.

An important part of USDA's general service lies in the distribution of information to the public. Each year it sends out millions of leaflets, bulletins, releases and factual communications. Among these are many which give specific, detailed directions for controlling pests. USE PESTICIDES WITH CARE—READ THE LABEL is continually emphasized. Here, for instance, is Home and Garden Bulletin No. 28, *Ants in the Home and Garden. How to Control Them*. After the clearly prepared, well illustrated text, in which some specific warnings are included, comes a section boldly headed PRECAUTIONS, which says:

> Most insecticides are poisonous to people and to animals. Keep insecticides where children and pets cannot reach them.
> Follow the directions and heed all precautions on the container label.
> Do not store insecticides with food. When applying them, do not contaminate water supply, food, dishes, or kitchen utensils.
> If liquid insecticide is spilled on the skin, wash it off promptly.
> Do not breathe the dust or spray.
> When you have finished applying an insecticide, wash all exposed surfaces of the body with soap and water. Wash hands and face before eating and smoking.
> Avoid drift into bee yards, adjacent crops, or pastures. Be careful not to get insecticides into streams, lakes or ponds.

When publications mention specific insecticides the precautions include clear advice for handling as well as applying them, along with instructions to follow in event of mishap.

The Department also sends out posters, television spot

films and tape, radio disks and movie film urging safer uses of pesticides.

The USDA's authority does not extend to the matter of policing the actual users of insecticides, and probably should not do so. As Secretary Orville L. Freeman has said, "The idea conjures up an unhappy image of a federal officer taking Mother Brown in for 'illegal' spraying of her roses."

The Food and Drug Administration, however, has authority to insure safety of the food supply, and lots of enforcement powers. This valuable, protective agency inherits its functions from the valiant fight that Dr. Harvey W. Wiley, when chief chemist for USDA, conducted to protect foods from adulteration and misrepresentation. These duties, along with others, now rest with FDA. The agency in 1965 had eighteen field offices and laboratories outside of Washington in which 707 scientists were employed. These are in addition to facilities in the capital city. If Mother Brown begins manufacturing her popular jellies or mince pies and shipping them across state borders, she can expect a call from one of FDA's 939 field inspectors, should any indication arise of misbranding or illegal ingredients.

Federal regulations, of course, apply only to materials shipped interstate, although interpretations of the constitution's commerce clause in recent years leave few transactions out of that category. States, however, have comparable laws and regulations, which further help to protect the public.

With regard to pesticides on food, the FDA inspectors do not always wait until an illegal shipment of contaminated food is ready to go. They check spraying and dusting practices in important areas to see whether, because of unusual growing conditions or carelessness, a crop may threaten to accumulate too much residue. Thus they help the grower by advising that he may avoid trouble by letting the crop weather longer or, if the crop is lettuce or similar, by adequate trimming. In a year (1963) FDA has examined 29,244 domestic samples for pesticide residues. Less than 3 per cent were found to bear residues in illegal proportions. Forty-two seizure actions were begun. These are regularly published in the *Federal Register,* as are administrative rulings and orders from all departments.

For further assurance that all legal protection will be extended to the public, an agreement among various agencies involved is in force, called the "Interdepartmental Coordination of Activities Relating to Pesticides." Participants in the agreement include the Fish and Wildlife Service from Interior, Public Health Service and FDA from Health, Education and Welfare, and Agricultural Research Service from Agriculture. This provides for a weekly exchange of information affecting pesticide activities, and steps to resolve conflicts or differences. In addition, a Federal Committee on Pest Control exists to consider broad policies and recommendations. This includes high officials from the three departments and also the Defense Department.

Buried among the scientific phrases in FDA technical reports one may now and then unearth a humanly interesting and highly important story. For example:

If you were to make a circuit of the United States every three months in company with a young human male, 16 to 19 years old, and feed him three choice meals a day, plus his snacks, and keep it up for two or three years, you would probably come up with a pretty fair idea of the foods around the country. And if, at the same time, you were prepared to analyze the boy's diet thoroughly, you would feel sure that you knew something about the safety and healthfulness of what people are eating.

The Food and Drug Administration has not done exactly that, but something equivalent or better. Four times a year for more than two years FDA people have gone into from two to four supermarkets in San Francisco, Minneapolis, St. Louis, Atlanta, and Washington, D.C. On each such visit they have purchased a supply of food such as would keep a 16- to 19-year-old boy happy for two weeks. The shopping list included some eighty-two different items. The list was based on the moderate-cost diet recommended by the USDA Household Economics Research Division. The items fell into eleven different categories: dairy products, grain products, root vegetables, leafy vegetables, smooth vegetables, potatoes, fresh and canned fruit, meat and eggs, sugar, fats and oils, dried beans and beverages. They bought milk, ice cream, soft drinks, roast and ground beef, pork chops, bacon, bread, butter, peanut butter, carrots, celery, peas, beans, corn, salad dressing, coffee, frankfurters, and candy bars. The vegetables were fresh, frozen, and canned.

The project really was started to find out how nuclear explosion fallout might be affecting foods—what amounts of strontium-90 and cesium-37 could be found. (The amounts were not alarming.) Then it was decided that as long as these carefully collected food samples were available, studies of the nutrients might as well be included, and that the residues from pesticides, if any, should be determined.

Without going into detail about the methods pursued, let it be noted that the latest and most sensitive procedures, including thin-layer and gas chromotography, were employed. Residues in terms of parts per billion could be identified. Had they been present, residues of twenty different chlorinated pesticides would have been detected.

A report upon the results said: "All pesticides detected in the foods as prepared for consumption were at very low levels, many at the minimum detectable by the methods used." Eight of the organic phosphorous type were noted and nine of the chlorinated pesticides, "all at extremely low levels." In other words, well below safe tolerance limits.

Foods were bought in Los Angeles, Kansas City, and Boston for a further similar study in 1964. "Pesticide levels found in the test samples were generally less than 7 per cent of the safe legal tolerance. Many of the most commonly used pesticides were not found at all," FDA reported. "The amounts . . . are insignificant from a health standpoint."

The mythical boy and his parents may well continue their travels and diet happily, and not only with assurance that they will not be poisoned; for the study also showed that the nutrient elements of the recommended diet are all there, un-affected by processing and preparation.

This widespread experiment suggests that the law, its ad-ministrators, the chemical makers and the chemical users all must be doing a good job at providing a safe and healthful food supply for the American consumers, all the nearly 200 million of them.

22/The Real Dangers

PERHAPS THE GREATEST SINGLE EVENT IN HUMAN HISTORY —and certainly one of the twentieth century's outstanding phenomena—has been the discovery that food can be plentiful. In the United States we have demonstrated that a populous nation can be fed with an abundant and healthful variety at an unprecedentedly low cost.

Only seven of each hundred Americans now engage in farming. So efficient is their production that for only one-fifth of take-home earnings the average family can enjoy an ample and well-balanced diet.

The so-called "surplus problem," perhaps largely political in character, represents a national blessing, far more endurable than a food deficit could ever be. The margin of production that runs 5 or 6 per cent above normal consumption arises from a relatively few crops; in the event that any disaster prevented annual renewal the carryovers could be exhausted within a matter of months. Because of political sensitivity, the surpluses have been expensive to taxpayers. That cost, however, would appear trivial in comparison to the prices food buyers would pay if, instead of a 5 per cent surplus, a 5 per cent deficit prevailed. A shortage of 5 per cent in foodstuffs could and quite likely would result in about 50 per cent increase in family food costs.

Advances on many fronts have made this economical abundance possible. Numerous improved techniques, including power and machinery, fertilizers, and better seeds, have played their parts. High among the progressive factors has been the tremendously greater ability to control insect and other pests. Without modern pesticides, some foodstuffs would disappear from the markets or be present only at much higher prices, and quality would become a conspicuous casualty.

Ill-founded pesticide legislation not based on scientific facts, and unwisely restrictive administration, would soon show themselves to be against the public interest. Steps have been suggested that would materially raise farm production costs and, consequently, food prices, with no benefit to consumers. Others would greatly increase the cost of bringing new and improved pesticides into use; here the effect would be to discourage the kind of private research enterprise that is highly essential to improve the present anti-pest weapons.

Pursuant to the controversies that varied reactions to pesticides have set in motion, the existence or the prospect of certain genuine dangers need to be recognized and forestalled.

Misinformation is perhaps the biggest peril—misinformation, lack of information, and misuse of information. Misinformation and ignorance can be far more "poisonous" to the public welfare than all the pesticides.

Few things in this world are easier to acquire than misleading information. The two delinquents out of a hundred juveniles receive publicity; the ninety-eight well-behaved youngsters are too normal to be mentioned. So the impression grows that all our teen-agers are in some way outrageous. A mere suspicion of a pesticide presence in a food product can be made into front-page news; the perfect purity and com-

plete safety of our daily food supplies hardly need to be
proclaimed. Press, television, and radio are not to be blamed
if some of us deduce wrong conclusions from this rumor or
that fact; they do not have the space or time to tell us all the
details or balancing factors, and if they did we still might not
pay attention.

If the general public is frequently misinformed, or given
impressions that lead to wrong conclusions, the long-run consequences can in more ways than one redound to its disad-
vantage.

Nevertheless an active propaganda, backed by a few facts,
no facts, or a little misinterpreted information, can alarm a
large number of people. Few of those on propaganda's receiv-
ing end are well enough armed with full truth to argue per-
suasively. Conversational remarks, even if factual, may not be
repeated correctly. Alarm is especially easy to propagate.
Build up enough of it in the atmosphere and someone wants
to pass a law; and there always are politicians who thrive on
alarm. Suggestions appear from time to time, some of them
plausible until carefully examined, that demand some analysis and public understanding.

As a chapter preceding this one indicates, we have in force
a number of excellent statutes which now protect health and
purse against almost any undesirable effect in the pesticide
field except the occasional individual carelessness or misuse
that no law whatever could prevent. When better laws can
be written, they will receive responsible support.

Foremost in consideration of the public interest stands the
supreme essential: an ample and healthful supply of food and
fiber for all the people.

For more than a century that essential has been the constant goal and responsibility of the U.S. Department of Agriculture. Our present abundance attests that USDA has done
well. Working with farmers, manufacturers, and trade agencies, it has helped all who participate in continuing to attain
that goal. Not only has it aided production; it has been vigi-

ABSENTEE REPORT

TEACHER'S NAME _____

HOME ROOM	DATE _____ 19___	
PUPIL'S NAME	ABSENT	REMARKS

Notebook - Take Home

lant to prevent impure, tainted or contaminated foods from reaching the markets.

USDA is not merely a farm agency. Its jobs are to serve all the people. USDA knows, of course, that unless farming pays food will not be forthcoming, and agriculture is its assigned area; but it must and does serve the whole public.

Proposals have been incubated that plan to place the entire federal jurisdiction over pesticides into another, perhaps a new, department, concerned with the "total environment" and not responsible to the people for their food supply. Some would transfer the registration of pesticides from USDA to the Department of Health, Education and Welfare, where Food and Drug Administration is responsible for tolerances but has no direct responsibility whatever for production. But the established arrangement, by which USDA, FDA and in some instances other agencies such as Public Health and Fish and Wildlife, participate in decisions affecting the public, has worked well. The combined judgments have provided factors that enjoined careful decisions on effectiveness, safety and wisdom.

Rash proposals such as these can be built up from propaganda and poorly analyzed information, and can gain a vociferous support. With plausible surfaces they may conceal different consequences than their proponents now anticipate or even worse results than their present opponents have conceived.

Especially when it has to deal with subjects that are in technical flux, the law itself can seldom be made nearly so perfect as can be desired. Few administrators in the federal executive departments have escaped perplexing problems that arose because the law was not clear and did not spell out or anticipate the precise action demanded under this or the other circumstance. The frequency with which courts have to interpret laws, or decide upon their validity, is proof of the law's frequent vagueness, uncertainty, or inapplicability.

To the "bureaucrats" this condition presents more or less

constant problems. When their jobs require that they enforce a law, they have no option but to do the best they can to follow the law's demands. Anyone who has known many of these men will believe that most of them are earnest, sincere servants of the public, sworn to their tasks of carrying out the laws Congress has imposed, and honorably devoted to the public interest. Naturally, being human, they vary in intensity of dedication and in capability of decision.

Two instances follow, which are presented here in order to display kinds of dangers that have in the past resulted, and may in the future appear, from literal reference to the law as written in Congressional committees, passed by the two houses of Congress, and signed by the President.

On November 9, as Thanksgiving time was approaching in 1959, the Secretary of Health, Education and Welfare held a press conference. Front pages across the nation reported his statements. He announced that some cranberries on the market had been found to carry a residue of a chemical that was considered to be capable of producing cancer.

The Secretary did not actually say that the cranberries in question would be hazardous to the health of anyone who ate them. His obligation, he said, "was to protect the health of the American people." He said that he intented to eat no cranberries himself until they had been cleared, and that those who ate them would do so at their own risk.

Growers used the offending chemical, aminotriazole, to kill weeds in cranberry bogs. When it was registered for this use in January 1958 by the U.S. Department of Agriculture, the directions prescribed applications at the rate of eight pounds per acre, seven to ten days after harvest. Applied accordingly, it was USDA's opinion that the following year's crop would present no danger to the user and no residue would appear.

Meanwhile, the aminotriazole manufacturers and the Food and Drug Administration had been subjecting the chemical to searching tests on rats and dogs. After a year the dogs showed no effects. Numbers of the rats, fed the material at the rate of one hundred parts per million, in two years had developed thyroid swellings. Swellings also appeared on rats fed smaller dosages but in decreasing numbers. Such two-year tests on rats are about equivalent to seventy-five human years.

On the basis of this evidence, FDA pronounced aminotriazole to be capable of producing cancer—a carcinogen.

The actual presence of hazard in the cranberries was sharply questioned. One authority, Dr. C. Boyd Shaffer of the American Cyanamid Company, who had supervised studies of aminotriazole, remarked that "a human would have to eat 15,000 pounds of (contaminated) cranberries a day for many years" to come near to the dosage and conditions experienced by the rats. Evidence then available and further developed later indicated that the chemical might produce goiter by inhibiting the thyroid from absorbing enough iodine; a result easily and completely reversible. Nothing has been adduced to suggest cancer.

What had happened, of course, was that a few growers in one northwestern area had improperly applied the weed killer, and in so doing had precipitated the entire upheaval. This misuse was a highly unlikely 1959 development, considering that from the 1957 crop, grown and harvested before FDA had made known its refusal to set a tolerance level for aminotriazole, the growers' cranberry cooperative had voluntarily held off the market and eventually buried some three million pounds.

The November 9 announcement by Secretary Flemming had been prompted when two out of the first several lots of 1959 cranberries offered for interstate shipment showed signs of "contamination," and a preliminary look at ten other lots had raised doubts.

The cranberry market, of course, immediately collapsed. More than two-thirds of each year's consumption takes place during October, November and December. The Flemming scare, spread before the nation two weeks and three days before Thanksgiving Day, accomplished an economic disaster for the entire cranberry industry. Sales fell to one-third of normal. The growers, small farmers in Massachusetts, New Jersey, Wisconsin, Oregon and Washington, were frightened. Many had received substantial advances from their cooperatives, which they could not afford to return.

Following the scare headlines of November 9 and 10, FDA was able to seize twenty-nine lots of cranberries and cranberry products which it charged were contaminated. The seizures amounted to about 300,000 pounds, or roughly one fourth of *one per cent* of the year's crop.

During the month prior to the cranberry boggle, FDA in its routine of law enforcement had seized other foods as unfit, mostly because of insect and rodent contamination, and some because they were short weight, misbranded, or below quality standards. Their October seizures had totalled 418 tons. Normally this would have been the procedure with cranberries or any other foodstuff with an illegal contamination. Reports of these actions appear regularly in the *Federal Register*.

Mr. Flemming's overanxious pronouncement was to cost U.S. taxpayers about $8,500,000 in cash. The cash was paid to growers who, through no fault of their own, had been injured by an official's statement. This was done under an existing law. The details were fully set forth in a June 1962 report to Congress by the Comptroller-General. In addition, USDA and other officials made vigorous efforts to restore confidence in cranberries, although the adverse affects continued to be felt by the industry for another year or so.

The merit of Secretary Flemming's zealousness must be said, at least, to be debatable; especially as reputable poison experts asserted that the dosage of aminotriazole required to produce the rat tumors was one thousand times heavier than the amount alleged to have been found on the seized cranberries. The idea accepted by the public was that a danger, not the mere marginal suspicion of a hazard, existed. The cost to farmers, even after some recompense from taxpayers, was substantial. Millions of consumers missed the healthful additional zest cranberries should have added to their holiday turkeys. And fuel was tossed upon the fretful flame always being coaxed to burn higher by misled opponents of pesticides.

Difficulties that may arise from rigidities of law are sharply brought out by recent episodes that have taken place in the dairy industry. Here it will be seen that both the bureaucracy and farmers were trapped. Heptachlor and dieldrin are effective in control of the voracious weevil that seriously damages alfalfa. Alfalfa is considered to be the finest and most desirable of all forages for dairy cattle. First registered for use on alfalfa in 1953, later withdrawn and then again authorized for southeastern and western areas, heptachlor had been applied by many dairy farmers. Again in late April 1963, USDA withdrew its approval of heptachlor and in July that of dieldrin.

No evidence had appeared that milk from cows consuming the treated alfalfa had become unsafe for people to use. But, under the law, FDA had required a zero tolerance. The methods of measurement in the earlier periods had indicated that no residues were present. When the newer, more highly sensitive tools became available, capable of detecting parts per billion, traces of residue could be and were discovered.

The law had not changed, but the scientific equipment had been improved.

The farmers had grown their alfalfa and put it into their barns entirely confident that they had used permissible insecticides in full compliance with the regulations then in force. When FDA intervened months later to say that their milk could not be marketed, they were not merely baffled; they were left without their dairy incomes, merely because of legislative and administrative complications.

Acting promptly upon protests from dairy farm organizations, Congress authorized an indemnity fund of $8,800,000 to reimburse farmers who had unjustly been victims in this episode of government confusion. Taxpayers, of course, contribute the $8,800,000. Farmers in Maryland, Virginia, Pennsylvania, Utah, West Virginia, Louisiana and Wisconsin were among those indemnified.

The basic question actually involved in the milk contretemps is whether these veritable traces, previously undetectable, offer any hazard to human health. Here all proof is absent. The obvious fact does stand out that no one is known to have been injured by using a dairy product at any time during the years these and various other insecticides have been in common use. Of course, if any evidence of danger can be discovered, it should be brought to light.

The Food and Drug Administration's surveys of marketed foods, including dairy products, across the country, as the 19-year-old-boy diet study reports, clearly confirm the safety of our three square meals a day.

The necessity for pesticides to protect and maintain the supplies for those meals stands uncontestable, at least until science finds other and better effective controls for the bugs, weeds and plant diseases.

It would seem logical, therefore, that any law should be so designed that a tolerance for any pesticide should be so set as to draw a line, a line wholly proper and sufficiently broad, between the safe and the unsafe. It should not require nor permit capricious action merely because still another new machine has become able to detect parts per quadrillion.

Concerned with this problem, the secretaries of Health, Education and Welfare and of Agriculture jointly requested the National Academy of Sciences to select a committee to study it. The committee of eminent scientists reported: "The concepts of 'no residue' and 'zero tolerance' as employed in the registration and regulation of pesticides are scientifically and administratively untenable and should be abandoned."

Another National Academy of Sciences committee, chosen at the request of the Food and Drug Administration, recommended in the summer of 1965 that the existing tolerances for aldrin and dieldrin, two "persistent" insecticides under attack, be continued at one-tenth of a part per million on raw agricultural commodities; and it suggested consideration of the same level for the uses where a lower tolerance is now prescribed. Advising further studies, it recommended that in three years a new committee review the facts that should be available by then.

One amendment now on the books, known as the "Delaney clause," could be interpreted as demanding that no compound should be permitted unless it can be proved not to cause cancer in humans as well as in animals. You can prove, perhaps, that something does cause cancer; to prove that it does not do so, beyond any possibility, would be an utterly hopeless undertaking. No one could even prove that plain water is never a carcinogen.

The serious dangers arise from the areas of public misinformation, misdirected legislation, and occasionally from administrative error. The sincerity and faithfulness to duty as they see it, on the part of most all career public administrators, does not deserve to be impugned. Because they use the counsel and experience of able staffs, their margin of human error is probably less than yours and mine. But they should not be asked to respond to unfounded fears nor to execute unreasonable law.

Unless it conspicuously affects large numbers of people, it is far harder to get a poor law changed than to get a good law passed. Once on the statute books, the law can have effects reaching farther into the future than the foresight of its authors may have done.

No legislator nor any responsible formulator of public opinion should overlook the fact that each year American farmers have three million or more new mouths to feed, and that our agricultural acreages will not expand. To maintain the present rate of abundance we shall need to make sensible choices; and wherever possible to make them at the expense of the pests rather than at the cost of impaired production and intolerable consumer prices.

23/What Needs to be Done?

WHAT, REGARDING PESTS AND PESTICIDES, SHOULD "WE, the people" concern ourselves about in this second half of the second decade of the twentieth century? Anything?

We should, indeed! Mainly we should be demanding prodigious amounts of research; demanding it from government, expecting it from industry, encouraging and supporting it in universities and institutions. So long as pests subtract from our economy huge agricultural and forest losses, obviously we do not have enough effective control over them. We should proceed to master our environment.

Despite the unprecedented progress in recent decades, the control yet to be desired can be measured only in figures of impressive magnitude:

More than three thousand different major insect species still damage crop plants to the extent of $4 billion or more each year.

The crop loss caused by several thousand fungal diseases stands around $3 billion a year.

Weeds that compete with crops mean a $5 billion loss.

Rats, mice, and other rodents do $2 billion worth of damage.

Nematodes probably reduce production by $1 billion a year.

Add to this $15 billion total the illness and injury among animals, plus the billion farmers and others have to spend for pesticides and their application, and we arrive at a staggering $17 billion estimate.

These are not just wild figures; nor can they ever be exact; they are careful estimates over which scientists and economists would not greatly disagree; some may say that they are too conservative. This is not so much as the national debt, but it is two-thirds the amount of the FBI's $27 billion estimate of the nation's crime bill. It is considerably more than the $12 billion net income of farmers. And it represents more than a fifth of what consumers pay ($82 billion government estimate for 1965) for their food—a 20 per cent plus food tax—which no one gets!

To combat these enormous losses, science has provided a mounting store of knowledge and some biological controls; chemical research has developed about three hundred basic molecular compounds which, in many variations, are our pesticides. (While thousands of pesticides are registered, all stem from the relatively few basic ones. Malathion, for example, has 137 registrations for various labels, formulations and purposes.)

Fully or partially successful though these instruments have been for many specific pests, they have served only to begin a brobdingnagian task, and to foreshadow that much of it may in time to be accomplished.

Can man anticipate a pest-free world? Can an American look forward to a pest-free nation here?

Probably not, ever.

Agriculture might possibly become free from weeds. They are not so mobile as insects. Rats conceivably could be exterminated if every town, city, community, and farmer determined to get rid of them. The means exist if the human will could be organized.

But few scientists would venture to predict the extinction of pest insects, fungal diseases or nematodes. They might look forward to very great advances in domestic animal health.

An unceasing probe to extract the innermost secrets of bugs and plants nevertheless goes on. Reinforcements in the forms of greater funds, new kinds of tools, and bolder ideas join and strengthen the attack. The insect has six legs instead of two, and must therefore have six Achilles' heels. Scientific arrows will find those vulnerable openings. The years ahead should disclose ways to deal with pests as new and revolutionary as was DDT in 1942.

The chemical poisons are likely for a long time to be the basic weapons in the endless antipest war. Today we use better ones than yesterday. Undoubtedly tomorrow will bring others more effective and more selective.

New techniques, moreover, in all likelihood will change some of the chemical approaches. Combinations of chemical and biological methods promise conspicuous advances.

For example, the synthesis of "gyplure" presages one such new shape of progress. The female gypsy moth was found to possess a substance that attracted—almost as if she were equipped with a magnet—the males of her species. The material was isolated, its chemical structure determined, and then successfully duplicated by synthesis of a related chemical structure. Traps baited with this chemical attractant quickly disclose whether the moths are in an area. Incipient outbreaks can be squelched before they spread far, or the male population destroyed as it concentrates around the lure.

The ladies of a dozen other destructive insect species are known to possess such natural sex attractants. As the chemical structure of these individual substances is disclosed, men will attempt to synthesize, and with that the possibilities for control or eradication brightens.

Some plant species, also, are already known to contain substances that lure insects to them. These substances, as well as the sex attractants, may eventually be synthesized and made into effective weapons.

Wherever an insect builds up large numbers, as many species do periodically, the present and future chemical controls will knock off the worst of an outbreak. Then, as the species population becomes considerably reduced, chemical attractants and sterilants may combine with smaller quantities of the poisons to attain a high degree of control. Eradications may more often be accomplished in situations where an exotic pest has not had time to spread too widely. Attraction by light and sound also are under study.

The prospect that natural populations may be sterilized chemically has gained acceptance from researches so far. Radiation sterility accomplished the screwworm eradication, but rearing the vast numbers required was expensive. Chemical sterilization is viewed as a much simpler process which, ideally, could lead to depletion or elimination of an objectionable species without using poisons.

Incidentally, the chemical manufacturers are not disturbed by nor do they oppose the study of biological controls. They do not expect that advances in this direction will put them out of a business that already is subject to frequent change; and they anticipate that in sterilants, attractants, or other devices they will find new opportunities. The prospects for greater successes as research receives more adequate support are encouraging on many fronts. The kinds of to-be-desired research are many.

More competent study in the broad field is going on today than ever at one time before. While Congress is seldom over-generous to research, except for health, military purposes, or space spectaculars, for decades it has consistently provided moderate funds for pest control studies. These have lately been increased and the objectives broadened. Not only government, but industries, universities, and some private insti-

tutions are exploring and probing for new facts; new fundamental studies are getting under way that will eventually pay
off in profitable new applications.

Fundamental research and applied research are distinct,
but the distinction is not always understood. If a scientist
takes five different insecticides, and tries them on potato bugs
at five different dosages each, he is doing applied research. He
is taking a fundamental fact and finding out how to use it.
He is working with already known facts, materials and techniques. But, a scientist may study the potato plant to find out
why it attracts that kind of bugs, or study the potato beetles
to find out why they prefer potato plants; if he does find out,
he will have discovered a new item of knowledge—this is
called fundamental research. Other scientists will likely find
a score of ways to *apply* that knowledge, not only to potatoes
but to other problems.

High urgency demands that much more knowledge than
we yet possess shall disclose what eventually becomes of pesticides. Where do they go in the air, soil and water, and what
do they do there? Exactly what happens as they enter into
insects, plants and animals, or as their fragmentary molecules
rise into the air? What is their long-run destiny and effect?

This area has deeply concerned the earnest people who
fear that pesticides are contaminating our environment to a
dangerous or, at least, needless degree, with occasional lethal
consequences to wildlife and conceivable or imaginary near-
or long-time hazards to human health.

One may easily enough dismiss some of these fears by re-
stating the well-attested fact that after a hundred years (and
more than a score since DDT) no known illness, much less no
human death, has been recorded that could be attributed to
any properly used pesticide. The concern about wildlife is a
little less easily dismissable, because fewer positive facts exist,
and no one wants to see avoidable fatalities or needless reduction of any species.

With respect to human hazard, regardless of the millions of

lives *saved* by pesticides and regardless of the wonderfully excellent record of safe usage, some types of people perhaps will never be freed from their apprehensions. Even though humans for three generations have been exposed and rats for fifteen or twenty, they will not be convinced that after fifteen generations people will not also be adversely affected. Even so, more research can and will diminish the numbers of the fearful.

Many phases of controversy about pesticide usages have emerged because research had not yet fully elucidated definite essential facts. The ablest controversialists, however, of whom we shall always have a number, are not always to be satisfied by facts, however obvious or definite. Some persons are still maintaining that no one can eat meat and remain healthy. A skilled controversialist can always ignore facts, divert attention from them, or twist them to his purpose. He can prove to his own satisfactions that if overdoses of DDT on Michigan State's elms killed robins, or overdoses of heptachlor killed snakes and quail in the early fire-ant campaign, pesticides ought not to be permitted anywhere at any time. Nevertheless, the higher the accumulation of incontrovertible facts, the less virulent will be the controversies and fewer misunderstandings will remain.

Merely to adduce an array of new facts to add to the vast store already available will not, however, be enough. We do have, as the previous chapter pointed out, a degree of danger from unwisely restrictive legislation that could greatly exceed any present or probable peril from pesticides. The danger here is that impossibly costly requirements, requirements that are not actually significant in relation to a pesticide's usefulness, effectiveness, or safety, may be imposed upon manufacturers and discourage or terminate their research progress. Public information and understanding can help to maintain correct and reasonable governmental attitudes.

The scientist who produces a new fact promptly announces

it in his favorite professional magazine, which reaches perhaps three or ten thousand of his fellow specialists. He proclaims his fact in a polysyllabic technical vocabulary, which conceals it perfectly from comprehension by any of us who read only ordinary English. By chance some science popularizer may discover and translate the discoverer's report in a newspaper column or magazine article. Then, and then only, does there begin to be an informed public; and only an informed public can effectively resist or help to resist hysterical pressures upon equally hysterical politicians (of whom happily not too many exist unless their majorities are threatened) to impose legislation that can restrict the orderly progress of science and industry toward still safer and still more effective ways of pest control.

New trails have been blazed in the direction of biological controls. Obviously these should be pursued by vigorous research efforts. The new USDA laboratory at Columbia, Missouri, will concentrate in this field, extending old work and developing new directions. No longer is this aspect limited to the introduction of predators or parasites. These had their limitations. When an introduction that fed only on one pest species reduced that creature's numbers to a minimum, it naturally itself began to run out of food and failed to reproduce in numbers. Birds are valuable predators upon insects, but if all the insects were eaten up how then would the birds live? In contrast, some of the new biological techniques lack those disadvantages.

Across the years the relationship between private and public research has been mutually advantageous, and profitable also to the public. When the industrial chemist brings out a new material from the laboratory and test fields, the federal and state experimenters frequently find new ways to use it and new ways to make it applicable. An outstanding example appeared when USDA scientists studied how to get the best use out of DDT and certain other insecticides early in World

War Two, when so many American soldiers were stationed in tropical and other infected areas. They came up with the aerosol "bomb," the device that in a few short years became a common household tool for scores of purposes.

The pesticide makers will be first to say that more research ought to be conducted on the application of their materials. They recognize that both aerial and ground applications by prevailing methods are imperfect. The drift of materials over to adjacent crops or waters where they are not desired still presents problems. Helicopters for some jobs have been found to be more exact and satisfactory than other aircraft. Precision of application assures better results and economy of materials. Where large areas are to be treated, such as the public forests, protective strips near streams and lakes are usually skipped to avoid water contamination; yet these strips then remain as sources for reinfestation. More research is needed to devise suitable formulations where extremely small dosages are sufficient for spreading over large areas.

As research expands a new problem arises—that of finding sufficient trained and capable personnel. Entomologists, pharmacologists, biologists, toxicologists and chemists of varied specialties will be increasingly in demand. Young people whose interest lies in the natural sciences will find ample opportunities for careers in some of these fields.

Long years ago a commissioner of patents advised Congress that a plan to erect a new building to house the patent office was superfluous. No need to spend the public's money, he said: the cotton gin, steamboat, railroad, and reaper had already been invented, it was unlikely that progress could advance further.

Today's amazing chemical aids to food production and health, like those inventions, represent but a fair beginning. Unfettered scientific enterprise will never be content with yesterdays nor even with todays. Better tomorrows are its unchanging goal.

24/A Cluster of
Reflections

IN THESE TURBULENT, AMAZING AND EVER-CHANGING times, few of us can hope to keep fully informed on everything that may exert an impact on our ways of living. Communications have become so overwhelming that we are deluged with facts and misinformation, with truths and with propaganda, and cannot always tell which is which. Populations explode, science reaches for the moon, wars threaten, fashions change, and the future for our children as well as for ourselves becomes harder to estimate.

Through these pages I have tried, within the space limits, to present a reasonable and balanced view of man's relations to the realm of insects and pests and to the measures he has undertaken for dealing with those populous provinces. To have described or even to have mentioned all the pests would have demanded encyclopedic space. No effort has been made to delineate all the pesticides and their known properties. Nor have I attempted to reply to all the fulminations of extremist critics, many of which are too trivial or unfounded to notice. Neither have I ignored those criticisms or questions that, in the present state of knowledge, seem to be warranted and legitimate. Many points could have been brought up, and some no doubt will be mentioned by others or will occur to readers, that did not seem essential to the book's intent.

In these final pages I wish to add a few further observations that do seem pertinent and have not found places in the earlier chapters.

No serious opposition to the general idea of chemical pesticides has ever been heard from anyone who looks realistically at his environment. Even emotional and unscientific critics usually concede that modern man must fight back against the worst of those foes that contest his necessity to use his chosen parts of the earth.

If any of the expressed fears and apprehensions are firmly founded upon fact, and if contamination of our environment is a serious prospect, certain considerations then become essential.

Is the contamination so serious as to injure human health and well-being in any way? No acceptable scientific evidence indicates this to be true. Repeated statements by the highest of health authorities declare that no single instance of authenticated illness, resulting from normal pesticide uses, has been discovered.

Is wildlife being poisoned out of existence or being adversely affected to an important degree? Evidence indicates that relatively little overall disturbance has been created by pesticides; that a few species may be imperiled by some cause, pesticides being one possibility; that a few localized instances are traceable to misuse or needless overdosage and that some of those reported are questionable. The injuries to wildlife from other acts of man, from what he has done to its environment, have been far more destructive.

What is a poison? When does a poison "contaminate"? The answers invariably depend upon the nature of the compound and upon the dosage. Salt and aspirin in big doses can be poisonous. Numerous drugs, chosen by physicians for medical purposes, are poisons, but exert no injurious effects in the amounts prescribed. Strychnine or arsenic, to cite simple examples, can be lethal in small excess, yet healing in certain instances. The sting of the honeybee injects a venom more poisonous than a cobra's, but the quantity is far less, and less enters the bloodstream.

Critics have worried that pesticide compounds may build up in the body until they will exert delayed, injurious effects. The human body has its own considerable built-in protections. A certain amount of DDT, for instance, will store up in fat; beyond a limited level the bodily processes cause it to be excreted, so that no known danger persists. For nearly two decades most of us must have been more or less exposed to DDT, yet for a dozen years the level in human bodies has shown no increase.

While several other motives actuate human behavior, the search for profit drives most of the economic machinery, pays most of the cost of government, keeps most of us in jobs, and provides the larger portion of philanthropic funds. Even in business, supposedly oriented solely to profits, other individual motives mingle—the aspiration to excel, the desire for prestige, the fascinations of a chosen activity, the obligations to employees and investors, and the satisfactions of providing goods or services which people need.

Pesticide makers have been accused of flooding the landscapes with dangerous products solely from the "sordid motive" of profit. Certainly none of the manufacturers would say that he would be in the business, or could stay in it, if no profits were possible.

The production of pesticides relatively is not a huge business. Only about forty companies are engaged. The total annual pesticide sales (in the $400 million range) amount to only about one per cent of the total chemical sales; and among

the larger companies who are leading makers, pesticides probably do not exceed 2 per cent of their totals. The big companies could abandon the business entirely without much
effect on their annual balance sheets.

Taking into account the several years of sustained scientific
effort, and the investment of from $2 million upwards, that
have to precede the introduction of a new pesticide, it would
be a foolish company that would then market a product if it
had any doubt about the need for it, about its effectiveness, or
any reason to anticipate unpredicted adverse results. The
countless safeguards established and enforced by law are
strongly reinforced by plain common sense.

The wants and needs incident to our American standards
of living are so many and diverse that, amidst our purchases
of what not so long ago would have been luxuries, we may
fail to notice that food, the basic necessity, comes so cheap.
We spend less for food than we pay out for taxes.

Families often calculate their food cost by adding the final
totals from their supermarket cash register slips. They forget
that the cart may have contained detergents, cleaning fluids,
paper supplies, cigarettes, comic books, flowers, phonograph
records, magazines, razor blades, toilet goods, or a dozen
other completely inedible items. After these are deducted a
family of average size with average income will find that only
about one-fifth (now less than 19 per cent) of the take-home
pay is spent for food.

In 1950 this figure was around 25 per cent. The rise in
farm pesticide use during the past fifteen years has been one
of the several factors contributing toward our low food
prices.

Figures from some other countries indicate that, compared
with our 19 per cent, that of Sweden is 27 per cent; Italy, 38
per cent; Japan, 42 per cent; West Germany, 45 per cent;
Russia, 56 per cent; Nigeria, 70 per cent. Most of the world's
people spend more than 50 per cent of their money and time
for food, many of them much more.

Those who worry about the alleged food-chain effects of pesticides may not be all wrong; large grants to several universities will help to find out whether they are, or are not. Meanwhile, another food chain possesses considerable interest to all of us.

That is the chain that reaches from the farmer to the family table. Concerned in it are all the farm suppliers, the truckers and railroaders, the processors, distributors, food stores, restaurants, and all the people. Let's use a trivial example; the principle is the same whether bread or meat is involved.

What happens if the California farmer-orchardist neglects to treat his pear trees properly and the little pear psylla takes over? Most of his pears will be too badly blemished and misshapen to sell. Consumers would not buy them and the stores would not even handle them. At an expense of time and money he might sort out and sell those that promise to pass inspection. The canners will not buy the injured fruit. Because fruit cocktails are prepared by machine, they can't even carve out undamaged portions from irregular fruit for that purpose. So the neglected pears pay no wages to transport workers, no wages to processing-plant employes, no wages to store clerks or anyone else. Proper insecticidal treatment could have put them usefully into the economic stream.

Such losses do occur, constantly, and not only at the farm level. The "one bad apple in the barrel" saying can apply literally to a case or a carload of perishable food materials, as the litter around any wholesale market is likely to prove. The apple is usually bad because it escaped the pesticide that would have prevented the bug, bacteria, or virus from spreading its injury.

To its every link, this food chain from farm to family has an especially high importance when one recalls that nearly 40 per cent of all economic activity—and of jobs—arises from farming, supplying farmers, and carrying farm products to consumers.

With food production the inescapable base upon which all economic progress, anywhere and everywhere, must be built and from which all cultures must rise; with human life and human health the utmost of our considerations; with all our hopes for a happier, though vastly more crowded world; with these and all our aspirations, be they the noblest or simplest, we shall do best not to ignore the pests that beset and bedevil human effort, health and life. Nor would we be wise to disdain either the hard facts about their multibillion-dollar yearly plunder, or about the grim campaigns to lessen their evils.

Appendix 1 / Quotations

The Basuto refuses to walk by a stream lest a crocodile should seize his shadow and consume it.

—Herbert Spencer

Yet only the esoterically inclined, I must insist, can look through what passes for matter and see that it isn't there!

—David Starr Jordan, *The Higher Foolishness*

Wishful thinking is by no means rare, even in academic circles.

—Charles MacFie Campbell

The broader pesticide problem in this country can be likened to the problem of sex. From the abuse of either sex or pesticides comes discomfort, disease, death, or grievous loss. From intelligent control of both comes much good, pleasure and productivity.

—*Journal of the American Medical Association,* January 4, 1965

A sense of proportion is very necessary here and I think that the lighthouse argument applies—no one suggests that we should pull down all our lighthouses because quite a number of birds dash themselves to death on them.

—Sir Harold Sanders, former Chief Scientific Adviser on Agriculture to the Ministry of Agriculture, Fisheries and Food

One of the major themes constantly recurring in the literature opposed to agricultural chemicals contends that only "natural" compounds are safe and that only "natural" controls of pests and diseases are really effective . . . There are, in fact, a whole array of well-accepted and long-used "natural" foods which are now known to contain appreciable amounts of suspect carcinogens, and doubtless many more will become known as food chemistry advances. A few familiar examples are tannic acid in tea, in nuts and in many fruits; capsicum in peppers; thio-urea derivatives in virtually all cole crops; arsenic in shellfish; selenium in many cereals, fruits and vegetables (which incidentally is quite possibly an essential nutrient for all warm-blooded animals, including man); cobalt in all meats (also a major component of vitamin B_{12} essential for blood formation); iron found in virtually all foods (and a component of human blood); estrogens found in all meats and also in humans. Whether such substances induce carcinomas or not depends, of course, upon a number of other factors, the principal one of which is dosage intake versus metabolism and elimination rate. Similar consideration belongs to all agricultural chemicals.

    —Dr. Robert White-Stevens, American Cyanamid Company

Pesticides are a great boon to mankind. We use them in and around our homes; they are used on farms; and they are used in many public health programs to prevent the spread of disease. You can yourself use pesticides with complete safety—if you follow the directions that come with them.
—Dr. David E. Price, Assistant Surgeon General, U.S. Public Health Service

Considered in its broadest scope, at the present time pesticides seem to be only minor influents in nature compared to other factors in land and water development and use. Urbanization, industrial pollution, drainage of marshlands, bringing land into cultivation—to name a few such factors—all constitute a greater hazard to wildlife survival than chemical use.
—R. L. Rudd and R. E. Genelly, *Pesticides: Their Use and Toxicity in Relation to Wildlife*. California Department of Fish and Game, Game Bulletin No. 7

The Council on Foods and Nutrition recognizes the contributions that chemical substances in food production, processing and preservation have made to the quality and quantity of the American food supply. While many chemical additives are essential to efficient agricultural production, others are vital to the manufacture of food products. There is no reason to believe that the present use of chemicals in foods is endangering the health of people. Responsible manufacturers have made careful safety tests before the introduction of new chemicals, and the Food and Drug Administration is diligently and effectively protecting consumers from presence of hazardous chemicals under existing federal laws.

—The Council on Foods and Nutrition of the American Medical Association, in the *Journal of the American Medical Association*, November 18, 1961

One irrefutable fact the critics of pesticides have been unable to answer in this true statement: there is not one medically documented instance of ill health in man, not to mention death, that can be attributed to the proper use of pesticides, or even to their improper use as far as ill health from residues on foods . . .

You can have confidence in our foods. They are not full of poisons as some food faddists would have you believe. They are nutritious and the quality is much better than it was a generation ago. Eat and enjoy them.

—Dr. Frederick J. Stare, Chairman, Department of Nutrition, Harvard School of Public Health

Appendix 2 / The Desolate Year

The *Monsanto Magazine*, a house organ of the Monsanto Chemical Company, St. Louis, published in October, 1962, the article that, with Monsanto's permission, is reproduced here.

THE DESOLATE YEAR

Does the world really need chemical pesticides? Are these compounds (used to control insects, rodents, weeds, parasites and plant diseases) better left alone? Is the public being sold a monstrous "bill of goods"?

The answers to those questions could be learned with finality by seeing what would happen if pesticides were not available. Imagine, then, that by some incomprehensible turn of circumstances, the United States were to go through a single year completely without pesticides. It is under that license that we take a hard look at that desolate year, examining in some detail its devastations.

Life-slowing winter lay on the land that New Year's Day, the day that nature was left to seek her own balance. Great drifts of snow cloaked the vast northland, and across the midsection of the country a thinner crust of whiteness was pierced by drab brown of brush and stone, naked tree, fence row and corn stubble.

Except for man's own small islands of sound and movement, most living creatures were silent, asleep. So it was that the grim reality of that defenseless year first sank home in the warm sub-tropics of lower Florida and California, Arizona and Texas.

It was warm that day in the citrus groves around Miami, and the glowing warmth drew a buzzing, harmless-looking fly from its place of rest. And she—for this was a female—was drawn into the golden air by some power that spanned the eons, that fur-ther drew her among the trees, and eventually to one weighted with growing grapefruit. The Mediterranean fruit fly turned her stiletto-like appendage into the first grapefruit, and when a tiny hole had been bored neatly through the rind, she sent an egg inside. Then she went to another, and another, taking no count of the eight hundred globes she had desecrated. Others of her kind, warmed and driven by the same purpose, followed; some further infested the holes she had bored, others sank new wells of their own.

Quietly, then, the desolate year began. Not many people seemed aware of danger. After all, in the winter, hardly a house-fly was about. What could a few bugs do, here and there? How could the good life depend upon something so seemingly trivial as a bug spray? Where *were* the bugs, anyway?

The bugs were everywhere. Unseen. Unheard. Unbelievably universal. On or under every square foot of land, every square yard, every acre, and county, and state and region in the entire sweep of the United States. In every home and barn and apart-ment house and chicken coop, and in their timbers and founda-tions and furnishings. Beneath the ground, beneath the waters, on and in limbs and twigs and stalks, under rocks, inside trees and animals and other insects—and, yes, inside man.

The most numerous and ferocious of all mankind's visible natural enemies lurked quietly that day, waiting. They weren't to be counted in the thousands, or millions, or billions. Nothing short of *trillions,* at least, could begin to account for their num-bers. They were there, as eggs or larvae or pupae or voracious adults—waiting.

In a small subterranean cubicle, hardly large enough for a man to move about in: 100,000 mosquito mothers-to-be, ready to fol-low those only basic drives of the insect, to live and reproduce. In one cornfield: tens of thousands of caterpillars, snug in the

balsalike interior of fodder into which they'd fed. Along the
sunnier south side of a single fence row in the Midwest: more
thousands of tiny white-winged black chinch bugs. Scattered and
broadcast across fields and meadows and ranges throughout the
country: uncountable masses of grasshopper eggs and nymphs.
Waiting.

But there is no more waiting for an insect when sun's warmth
stirs it from its lethargy. Nor need there be any waiting when
the warmth is otherwise available.

Thus, even as the Florida citrus grower stood petrified, a
pierced and wormy grapefruit in his hand and the frightening
Medfly flitting through his trees, a New York housewife caused
more widespread alarm. Her apartment was crawling with ticks—
supposedly harmless dog ticks that her pet had transferred there
from Central Park. What could she do?

What *could* she do? For, without pesticides, the pest control
firms had automatically gone out of business. Of a sudden, some
of the starkness of the times dawned on other people. No more
protection against moths in clothing, furniture, carpets; no
weapon but a fly swatter against rampant bedbugs, silverfish,
fleas, slithering cockroaches and spreading ants. More people
shuddered, then, and still the desolate year was young.

Desperation grew in Florida; infested trees were hacked and
burned and the diseased fruit consigned to the flames. The Medfly produced and reproduced and spread, bent on making every
orange and lemon and grapefruit over millions of acres so mas-
sively infested with maggots that humans would not ship or can
or freeze or eat them.

Other insects brought other diseases to the ruined citrus, and
the Floridians could not even find consolation in the fact that
the great burden of scales and blights, blisters and scabs was like-
wise killing off rival groves in California and Arizona.

The garotte of nature rampant began to tighten. The winter
vegetables of the sunlands were barely marketable. But the next
early crop was plagued. First to feed were the unseen cutworms,
rasping off tender stalks below the ground. Then the mites and
aphids, and the pretty butterflies that winged over the fields—
and dropped eggs onto cabbage and cauliflower and broccoli and
kale. Green worms, tan ones, striped ones, spotted ones, all

hungry and eating, leaving their various residues in labyrinthine runways inside fruit and in crotch of stripped stalk. Finally, the beetles and bugs and skeletonizers ripped the leaves from potatoes and bush beans and limas, and their fellow workers in the field invaded hull and pod, and infested them with eggs and other matter.

So went the fresh, clean vegetables.

So went sweet corn, for that year hardly an ear from corner to corner of the nation brimmed with just its own sweet juice. If its stalk and ear escaped the harsh attack of the borers, along came the earworm, hatching from eggs that a brown-gray moth slipped into the receptive silks alongside the life-giving pollen. Her worm children ate and defecated and ate more, working from the tender small kernels down into the large firm ones.

So the farmers planted and cultivated, and too often the harvest was garbage. The men at the packing plants and canning plants groaned. How could such refuse, even though whittled and carved and cored by hand, be cleaned and processed and pass for good food?

Inspectors for the Food and Drug Administration asked the same question, and were stumped for an answer. They couldn't approve food products containing what some of these did. But people had to eat. As food grew scarcer, prices spiraled.

It was a problem that grew; things got much worse that year. For now spring came to America—an extremely lively spring.

Genus by genus, species by species, subspecies by innumerable subspecies, the insects emerged. Creeping and flying and crawling into the open, beginning in the southern tier of states and progressing northward. They were chewers, and piercer-suckers, spongers, siphoners and chewer-lappers, and all their vast progeny were chewers—rasping, sawing, biting maggots and worms and caterpillars. Some could sting, some could poison, many could kill.

Hard-pressed men of the U. S. Department of Agriculture, besieged with pleas for help, could only issue advisories to rake and burn, to plant late or early, to seek the more resistant strains. But when insects and diseases took over anyway, there was no recourse.

In nook and cranny and open field where plants were just in

bud, the insects bred and re-bred, cross-bred and in-bred. Some didn't breed at all, or need to; females simply produced more females which gave birth to more hordes of females.

The insect hosts descended in earnest. Here are just a few of the things that happened:

A cattleman in the Southwest rubbed the back of a big red steer, and his hand found two large lumps under the hide. Sick at heart and sick at stomach, the man looked at the hairy flies swarming around his herd.

Then, gritting his teeth, he placed his thumbs at the sides of one of the lumps and pressed. The hair parted, a small hole opened and stretched. A fat, brown inch-long maggot slowly eased through the hole. It fell to the ground and the man stepped on it. One insect controlled.

But there were too many thousands of cattle grubs that year for such counter-measures. The flies buzzed and laid their tiny eggs on the animals' "heel" hairs. The eggs hatched into small and ugly organisms that bored through the skin and coursed around the cattle's bodies between muscles and skin to the back—small moles moving under golf tees of sleek hair. There, they bored air-holes that damaged the hide for leather; infested the finest meat of the animal. Finally, each grub forced its air-hole open, pushed itself out and fell to the ground, another heel fly in the making.

Cattle—and sheep and hogs and fowls—suffered mightily that year. Ticks clamped onto their flanks and flies clouded their eyes. The screwworm flies planted their eggs in the scratches and sores that the others made. The screwworms ate out massive wounds that invited still more maggots. Many whitefaces died that year, and many cattle of other breeds.

But food and fur animals weren't the only ones that died to the hum of the insects that year. Man, too, sickened, and he died.

Some people retreated to the coolness of the mountains to pitch their tents, although life outdoors was beset by whirring gnats, flies and mosquitoes that summer. Among them was a man who had returned from a sojourn in the Far East. One day, he was stricken by an old foe that had returned violently—malaria.

While he suffered, the mosquitoes kept biting, and as each

keen proboscis siphoned off his blood it also sucked in deadly gametocytes that were in the red corpuscles. Inside the mosquitoes, after a complicated reproductive cycle, microscopic organisms split and multiplied within their own expanding walls until, after two weeks, the walls broke. Out of each came thousands of minute sporozoites to circulate through the host insect, to settle in the salivary glands.

Unmolested, the mosquitoes whined over the mountainside, piercing and sucking. Each time a proboscis plunged into a camper, a droplet of saliva was forced in, too—nature's way to make the blood flow freely. And in some of the droplets, there lived malaria.

Half a dozen campers, infected by the first onslaught of the host mosquitoes, suffered the fiendish torture of chills and fever and the hellish pain of the world's greatest scourge. Eventually, nearly three dozen people were brought down, and no one knew how many mosquitoes had bitten how many of the new patients, and so had become able to spread the outbreak further. Who could curb the mosquitoes?

South and West, in the miles and miles of cotton fields, the situation went beyond control. The worst plant-loving demon of them all chewed into the tender squares of young cotton plants. The long-snouted boll weevil, tragically belying her comical mien, inserted one egg into each of the meekly vulnerable buds after she ate, and the eggs ushered in disaster.

Three days as eggs, ten as greedy larvae hollowing out square and boll, four more as pupae, and the new boll weevil generation bored its way out, mated, and sought out every undamaged boll to deposit more eggs. Not very many bolls were left for them, however, because the bollworm—thief of several aliases—had moved in, too, chewing its way in and out of boll after boll. Nor had these co-wreckers the fields to themselves; the dreaded pink bollworm broke from the confines where it had fought desperately for fifty years and joined in to destroy the seeds themselves.

So went the vital cotton crop. So went the apples and pears and peaches; they had no chance from the start, because the numbers and deadliness of the insect enemies of fruit and berries were simply overwhelming—a bewildering battery of scales, aphids, mites, borers, curculios, moths, maggots, hoppers, thrips, beetles, slugs, flies, chafers, worms, rollers, grubs and weevils.

A plant plague came too, that year, adding its weight to the growing burden. Weed and insect raced each other for strawberry patch, garden plot and field of grain. They both emerged as victors in the jungle-like snarl of the strawberry runners and thick stands of wheat and rye. Tough grasses—crab, foxtail and Johnson—grew sometimes as rapidly as corn, and whole fields were abandoned to them. Thistles and wild oats could not be pulled successfully by hand in the grain and flax fields; it would have been far too costly, anyway.

Unneeded and unwanted insect reserves poured into the fray, and for man the outlook became bleak, indeed. For now came the turn of the grasshopper, most awesome plague of the plains and heartlands of America.

The hoppers never had been shy, and this year they rushed on, unchecked, in churning, boiling clouds that blotted the sun. Arizona, Colorado, Nebraska, Oklahoma, Kansas, Missouri. A hundred of them to the square yard. The remains of alfalfa, clover, soybeans and garden vegetables, already ravaged by their "own" caterpillars, seed midges, plant lice, mites, slugs and skippers, were pillage for the grasshoppers. In many places, the clicking swarms completely denuded the land of vegetation, and moved on.

On they went into the cornlands of the Midwest. But much of the corn was already doomed, doomed from the time the ant-aphid teams moved in to feed on its roots until the European borer wriggled and ate in the stalks and the earworms lay waste to the milky kernels.

The Eastern truck farmers had to give up, too. Tomatoes, sweet peppers, beans, sweet corn, cucumbers, melons—deformed, wormy, rotting on the vine. Half their tomato crop disappeared in the wilting yellow and brown leaves of blight alone, and the worm makers sought every break in the skin of the fruit that lived.

Beetle and worm fed on top and tuber of the potato, from Idaho to Maine. Then the really notorious villain, Ireland's awful late blight, took over, and the firm brown "spuds" were gone, turned into black slime.

Enough? No; it should be remembered well, this terrible year of the insect and rodent and weed. How the termites felled innumerable buildings, destroyed a state's valuable papers, wiped out a library, brought a service station tumbling down. How the great forests wilted; how tent caterpillars stripped every leaf from eight hundred acres of trees in one place, and masses of beetles beneath the bark killed off six thousand pine trees in another.

The mosquitoes were everywhere, and no one knows what harm they did—sixty thousand cases of "breakbone fever" in Galveston and Houston alone. Half a million cases in Texas. How many others across the country? How many epidemics, and what kind, did they cause? Yellow fever hung like a specter over that enormous "receptive area" of the southern U. S., and public health officials dreaded the day when some infected person might arrive at a dock or airport in that region. Only the mosquito, transmitter of a dozen human diseases, could launch an epidemic of deadly yellow fever.

And the ticks leaped onto people. While the sharp and grasping pincers held fast, the razorlike cutting tools sliced deeper and deeper into the flesh. The ticks gorged that year, until they were many times their normal size, and many left disease and death behind. Rocky Mountain spotted fever, Colorado tick fever, "Q" fever, relapsing fever, tularemia. Some of them just as painful as malaria, and some more lethal. How many thousand cases were there? And the tick paralysis that also killed, if the animal weren't torn from its hold on scalp or neck or spine.

There was more that year, far too much to tell. The invading fire ants, for instance, which someone once pictured as minor pests at worse and not worthy of full-scale extermination. They sent three hundred people to the hospital in just one community, and all but killed three of them. They killed fish that ate them. They marched on.

The fine lake trout was turned back to the rasping, bloodsucking lamprey that once had riddled its numbers nearly to extinction, and the species began to die off again. Weeds clogged streams and lakes again, and harmful plants reclaimed the duck marshes and feeding grounds that had been so carefully managed.

Finally, of course, there was the chilling news that spread as a wracked nation surveyed the damage: there could be no falling back on much of the surplus food in storage. Practically no farm commodity could be stored in its natural form and not be vulnerable to contamination by other dozens of kinds of insects and their numerous aides. Rats and mice multiplied prodigiously. Freed from pesticidal opposition, they, too, burgeoned in elevator, bin and crate. And what was left was hardly food.

What, at the end of such a year, would be the fate of the United States of America?

NOT FICTION . . . FACT

The terrible thing about the "desolate year" is this: Its events are not built of fantasy. *They are true.*

All of them, fortunately, did not take place in a single year, because so far man has been able to prevent such a thing. But all the major events of the "desolate year" have actually occurred. They occurred in the United States. They could repeat themselves next year in greater magnified form simply by removing this country's chemical weapons against pests.

ITEM: In April, 1929, the Mediterranean fruit fly was discovered in Florida grapefruit. It spread over ten million acres of citrus and threatened to wipe out the entire industry. Lacking modern technology, six thousand persons carried out a $7 million eradication program, a large part of it the destruction of infested trees and fruit. When the fly appeared again in 1956, it was eradicated by eight hundred men utilizing chemical attractants in plastic traps and large-scale spraying and baiting with modern insecticides. Another appearance in June, 1962, was stamped out by the end of July. At present, the U.S. is the world's only source of worm-free citrus fruit.

ITEM: Field tests and careful studies indicate that no commercial crops of apples, peaches, cherries, sweet corn, grapes, strawberries, cranberries, raspberries, potatoes, tomatoes, carrots, kale, mustard, collards, spinach and other food plants could be grown in this country without chemical insecticides and/or herbicides.

ITEM: One hundred cattle grubs are often found in the back of an untreated animal, reducing milk flow by as much as 25 per cent, drastically damaging the hide for leather and ruining several pounds of meat. Three-fourths of the nation's cattle may be infested with them, even with treatment available, and the annual loss due to the grub is probably over $100 million. Screwworms attacked more than 1,350,000 animals in the Gulf states in 1934, killing more than 200,000.

ITEM: The boll weevil has done an incredible amount of damage to cotton in the U.S., once leaving entire counties destitute. Given one female weevil at the start of a season, she and her offspring will produce two million weevils by fall under ideal conditions! Even with the best defenses available, they destroy three to five million bales of cotton yearly, and since invading this country have cost Americans at least $5 billion. Each year, despite controls, they will still cost each of us $10 or more.

ITEM: In July, 1952, a returned Korean war veteran with malaria suffered a relapse while camping near a Camp Fire Girl retreat in the California mountains. Mosquitoes that bit him during the relapse transmitted malaria to nine other persons, who suffered attacks that fall; the next spring, twenty-five more people came down with the disease in various parts of the state. All cases were traceable to the original patient. As late as 1935, there were 900,000 cases of malaria in the U.S., with four thousand deaths. Modern insecticides, particularly DDT, have played a key role in practically stamping out the disease in this country —and in twenty-three others.

ITEM: In 1874–76, grasshoppers swept across the western states, particularly Kansas, Colorado, Nebraska and Missouri, in an invasion that caused over $200 million damage and was termed a national disaster by Congress. Many other serious outbreaks have occurred in the years since, with damages running into untold millions of dollars. An infested acre sometimes is alive with sixteen bushels—two million—grasshoppers, and they are known to strip more than 99 per cent of all vegetation from some areas. A

Utah county paid bounties for over two billion dead grasshoppers in a single year.

ITEM: Before chemical pesticide controls of any kind, nearly a century ago, the ravages of chinch bugs, grasshoppers, army worms, potato beetles and other hosts of insects literally forced many farmers to sell out or abandon their land in the Midwest. It was there, in 1867, that Paris green was used in the first large-scale application of an insecticide; man's effective defenses against insects date from that time.

ITEM: The European corn borer alone attacks at least two hundred kinds of plants, and has literally destroyed many crops. Thousands of acres of sugarbeets have been abandoned to webworms. Blight has destroyed half the tomato crop in the East (1946), and cracked or torn fruit, even in transit from field to processing plant, has been infested by several hundred eggs and larvae per tomato by the drosophila fly.

ITEM: Successful production of potatoes has depended on chemical pesticides since 1870. Spreading across the U.S. at the rate of eighty-five miles per year, the Colorado potato beetle decimated the crop until Paris green checked it. Without pesticides, the potato crop also is subject to the same late blight that caused the notorious famine of 1845 in Ireland. Ironically, Europeans have been reduced to eating insects only once—in Ireland, during that famine.

ITEM: Termites alone destroy more wood annually than all the howling forest fires, and in combination with other insects cause from seven to ten times the damage of the destructive flames. Among their depredations, they have destroyed a collection of books and papers of Illinois, ruined a school library in South Carolina during the summer recess, gutted a government vault and brought a California service station crashing down, triggered by a truck's noise.

ITEM: Just two cases in the annals of forest protection describe an eight hundred-acre block of quaking aspen completely denuded by tent caterpillars (and restored to health by aerial spraying) and of 6,722 lodgepole pines in one forest section laid low by the bark beetle.

ITEM: Tick-borne diseases have been reduced and their fatality

rate lowered in the U.S. by inoculation, antibiotic drugs, insecticides (against ticks) and rodenticides (against rats and other
rodent reservoirs). Yet cases—and deaths—still occur. At least five
men working at eradicating spotted-fever ticks and host animals
in the West have themselves been stricken with the disease and
died. The fever has spread across the country, and the dog tick
has become a vector. Typhus, with a mortality rate as high as 70
per cent and for which no successful treatment is known, has
been controlled in the U.S. largely by insecticide eradication of
body lice. At least twenty-five kinds of fleas living on rats and
wild rodents can transmit bubonic plague—the "black death"—
and large areas of the U.S. are endemic (rodents and fleas there
are infested).

ITEM: Mosquito-borne St. Louis encephalitis, which appeared
as an epidemic in that city in 1933 with more than one thousand
cases, struck Hidalgo County, Texas, in 1954. Of six hundred
patients, at least two died. Physical eradication of the mosquitoes
was found impossible, and a continuing insecticide control program was put into effect. An outbreak of the disease in Florida
in the summer of 1962 caused several deaths. Equine encepha-
lomyelitis, also mosquito-borne and highly fatal to horses
(400,000 of them suffered from it in 1935–39 in America, and
33,000 were killed by it in 1937 in Kansas alone), has become a
human disease and in the great outbreak of 1941 it struck three
thousand persons in three upper midwestern states and Canada.
In 1922, mosquitoes launched an epidemic of less serious dengue
fever which ultimately affected as many as 600,000 Texans alone.
The entire southern third of the U.S. has been designated a
"receptive area" for yellow fever by the U.S. Public Health
Service because of the abundance of mosquitoes capable of transmitting the disease.

ITEM: The imported fire ant, still relentlessly marching northward through the Gulf Coast states, invaded Fort Benning,
Georgia, in 1956, and eventually three hundred persons were
treated for stings. Three cases could have been fatal without
prompt attention—a girl and two middle-aged officers, all of whom
suffered violent reactions to the ants' poison. Fifty tons of insecticide finally rid the post of the ants.

ITEM: Sea lampreys, which attach themselves to, and feed on, valuable fish, are being brought under control after threatening to eliminate the lake trout from the Great Lakes. A special chemical pesticide has proved the only effective means of killing the lamprey. Wildlife and conservation groups have made wide use of chemical pesticides to improve the habitat of fish and game; an example is widespread utilization of herbicides to free marshes and waterways of undesirable vegetation.

ITEM: Insects take a $500,000,000 annual toll of food and fiber in storage and transit, even with controls used now. Rats ruin up to $2 billion worth of food each year, are carriers of at least six diseases, and have attacked—and killed—many humans.